AGE OF THE
ṚGVEDA

BY

DR. NARENDRA NATH LAW, M.A., B.L., PH.D.,

Premchand Roychand Scholar, Calcutta University.

Author of

Studies in Ancient Hindu Polity, Promotion of Learning in India during Muhammadan Rule, Promotion of Learning in India (by Early European Settlers up to 1800 A.D.), Aspects of Ancient Indian Polity, Inter-State Relations in Ancient India, etc.

FIRMA K. L. MUKHOPADHYAY

CALCUTTA : : 1965

20/-

Published by
Firma K. L. Mukhopadhyay
6/1A, Banchharam Akrur Lane,
Calcutta-12.

Price Rs. 15·00

35/-

Printed by
Sri J. C. Sarkhel
at Calcutta Oriental Press Private Ltd.
9, Panchanan Ghose Lane,
Calcutta-9

AGE OF THE
ṚGVEDA

DEDICATED

TO

THE MEMORY OF

Prof. Benoy Kumar Sarkar, M.A., for his strenuous efforts to extend the bounds of economic literature in Bengali through his monthly Journal, "*Ārthik Unnati*" for about 24 years from 1926. It was fortunate that I could extend my full co-operation to the erudite scholar in his cultural and literary activities.

Narendra Nath Law

Author, Dr. N. N. Law, is one of the old guards of Indological studies and his is a name to conjure with. He is the Founder-Editor of the *Indian Historical Quarterly* which was started in 1925 and has been continuing up to the present day. The Journal has earned high reputation not only in India but also abroad. His contributions in many fields of Indian History have won for him the position an eminent historian at the various centres for studies in Indian History & Culture. It is our proud privilege to be associated with him and to be of some humble help to scholars in India as also in countries through publishing his later works and issuing editions or reprints of his earlier books like *Studies in Ancient Hindu Polity, Promotion of Learning in India during Muhammadan Rule, Promotion of Learning in India (by Early European Settlers up to 1800 A.D.), Inter-State Relations in Ancient India, etc.*

PREFACE

1. In the nineties of the 19th century, a hot controversy raged round the problem of the determination of age of the *Ṛgveda.* It was B.G. Tilak who set the ball rolling in 1893 by publishing his famous *Orion,* in which he tried to prove the antiquity of the Veda by means of literary and astronomical evidence, viz. that it began in 4000 B.C.

2. Absolutely in an independent way, working at Bonn, far away from Poona where Tilak had his residence, H. G. Jacobi had arrived almost at the same time at a conclusion by his careful study of the Vedas and the Brāhmaṇas that the ancient Indo-Aryans knew of a Nakṣatra-series viz. the Mṛgaśiras-series older than the Kṛttikā-series which lasted according to Tilak from about 5000 B.C. to 3000 B.C. in which the *Ṛgveda* was composed. Jacobi was of opinion that the beginning of Vedic literature should be placed in 4500 B.C.

3. In September, 1892, Bühler received, from the Committee of the Ninth International Oriental Conference in London, the *Orion* of Tilak in manuscript. He was requested to give his opinion for its inclusion in the *Transactions* of the Conference. The contents of the book surprised him very much, for he found that the views of Tilak agreed closely with those of Jacobi, and that Tilak had quoted some of the passages that Jacobi had discussed previously with Bühler in Bonn. Bühler recommended inclusion of the *Orion* in the *Transactions,* as it was a new discovery, but only an abstract of the *Orion* could be printed in the *Transactions* for want of funds. Bühler received 2 copies of this abstract in November 1892, and sent one of them to Jacobi.

4. Tilak's *Orion* was printed and published in book-form in 1893, and Jacobi's article entitled *On the date of the Ṛgveda* was published in the *Indian Antiquary,* June, 1894.

5. Bühler's reaction to the almost identical views of the two scholars resulted in the publication of his "Note on Professor Jacobi's Age of the Veda and Professor Tilak's Orion" in the *Indian Antiquary,* 1894 (September), in which he declared that both of them had made good their main proposition, viz. that the ancient Indo-Aryans had once an older Series of the Nakṣatras

with Mṛgaśiras at the vernal equinox. He did not of course agree with all the views expressed by the two scholars, but he held that their main proposition was correct. He pointed out his difference with them in some details.

6. Both Whitney and Thibaut strongly criticised Jacobi and Tilak, but their manners of criticism were different. Whitney's arguments were straight and clear-cut. He was comprehensive, but did not go to import any extraneous matter as Thibaut did (e.g. the latter's treatment of a passage from the *Kauṣītaki-Brāhmaṇa*). Whitney demanded outright that certain conditions must be fulfilled before he could accept the truth of the theory propounded by Jacobi or Tilak. He thought that the conditions had not been fulfilled, and so he was at liberty to reject the views of Jacobi and Tilak on the antiquity of the Vedas.

7. Thibaut's treatment was not like Whitney's. He devoted the major portion of his arguments to a detailed examination of the theory of year-beginning, as propounded by Tilak and Jacobi, the main reason being that once he could prove that the ancient Indo-Aryans had no fixity of time in beginning their yearlong-Sacrifice and therefore the year, the theory of the familiarity of Indo-Aryans with Mṛgaśiras-series would fall to the ground. Both Whitney and Thibaut had poor opinion of the Astronomy of the ancient Indo-Aryans. While Whitney threw a challenge to Jacobi and Tilak in the manner mentioned above, Thibaut made the *Kauṣītaki-Brāhmaṇa* (not used by Jacobi or Tilak) and *Jyotiṣa-Vedāṅga* (both of which he placed together at a much later date).

8. Though the controversy stopped abruptly after the publication of Thibaut's article in the *Indian Antiquary* in 1895, it appears that Tilak found no reason to change his opinion regarding the antiquity of the Veda. He must have seen all the criticisms levelled against himself and Jacobi and yet in 1903 he declared the date of the *Ṛgveda* to be much over 4000 B.C. in his book "the Arctic Home in the Vedas."

9. As far as is known, no systematic attempt had been made during the last 70 years or so, to examine the validity or otherwise of the arguments of Whitney and Thibaut against Tilak. Sporadic discussions on one or other item of Tilak's *Orion* have appeared from time to time in different Oriental journals in India, without any comprehensive study of the whole matter. Tilak has adduced astronomical evidence from Vedic literature in proof of his thesis, but not to the exclusion of literary one. His interpretation of Ṛbhus, Vṛṣakapi, Frog-song, Upākaraṇa and Nakṣatra-series

throw a flood of light on the difficult problem of the date of the *Ṛgveda.*

10. The views of Tilak and Jacobi regarding the age of the *Ṛgveda* and of Bühler in their support and of Whitney and Thibaut in their opposition, have been put together and examined here in detail for the first time. The thread of the discussions of the great scholars, left interrupted by death of some of them, has now again been taken up in order to reach a rational conclusion. Tilak's theory on the antiquity of the *Ṛgveda* in the light of all the criticisms levelled against him has been critically analysed and found to be correct.

11. In this connection, we should gratefully remember Max Müler, one of the greatest Oriental scholars, who did so much to recover the Vedic texts and to encourage their proper study. Indeed at the time when he wrote, it was difficult for anybody to declare even that the *Ṛgveda* had been composed in 1500 B.C. According to Max Müller the *Ṛgveda* was the oldest possible literary relic chronologically existing. He was however of opinion in 1890 that "Whether the Vedic hymns were composed 1000, or 1500 or 2000 or 3000 years B.C. or earlier no power on earth will ever determine" (*Physical Religion.* p. 14), thus admitting the possibility of 3000 B.C. or earlier as the date of the *Ṛgveda.* Tilak, in his later work, *The Arctic Home in the Vedas* (1903), pushed further back this date to 5000 B.C.

12. Tilak used 542 passages from the *Ṛgveda*, 77 of which he interpreted differently from Yāska and Sāyaṇa. In this work, the time of the composition of the *Ṛgvedic* verses was placed in the Mṛgaśiras Nakṣatra epoch (Orion Period) which extended from 5000 B.C. to 3000 B.C.

13. The important passage in the *Taittirīya-saṃhitā.* VIII. 4.8 (and the similar one in the Tāṇḍya-Brāhmaṇa, V. 9) led Tilak in his *Orion* to the conclusion that the Gavām-ayana or a similar sacrifice, which was the counterpart of the year, commenced from an equinoctial point (i.e. vernal equinox) and that the ancient Indo-Aryans pointed out Nakṣatra-Series not only with Kṛttikās at the head, but also with the older Mṛgaśiras at the head. Mṛga(śiras) is mentioned in the *Ṛgveda* to indicate 4000 B.C. or thereabouts (Vide *the Orion*) changed later on to 5000 B.C. by Tilak himself in his *Arctic Home.* Tilak takes up in the *Orion* the Rgvedic songs on Ṛbhus (1.161), on Vṛṣākapi (x. 86), and on Maṇḍukas (vii. 103), and shows how they support his theory in regard to the antiquity of the *Ṛgveda.*

14. Whitney did not directly deny the correctness of Tilak's interpretation of the said passage of the *Taittirīya-Saṃhitā*. He stated that he would admit the theory of Tilak, if the latter could prove that Vedic literature contained evidences in support of what he had said viz. that the Sattra is the counterpart of the year, that Viṣuvat divides the year in two equal halves and therefore is at vernal equinox, and that the Mṛgaśiras and Kṛttikā-series are indicative of two earlier and later periods of time known to the Indo-Aryans. In regard to auxiliary evidences advanced by Tilak in the *Orion*, Whitney denied that 12 days' sleep indicated a twelve days' intercalation and their awakening on the appearance of the Dog (star), a year-beginning in the Mṛgaśiras period ; and that the Vṛṣākapi hymn referred to Mṛga(śiras), it being according to Whitney nothing but a picture of a quarrel between Indra and Indrāṇi on ape-man. He also rejected Jacobi's interpretation of the Maṇḍuka-Song (specially VII-103.9) and stated that it had no reference to the beginning of the year in the rainy season in some remote age. In opposition to Jacobi, he further maintained that the Upākarana could be celebrated any time of the year and had no connection with the year-beginning.

15. The present dissertation shows that the conditions required by Whitney for his acceptance of Tilak's theory had been fulfilled and that theory was corroborated by the auxiliary evidences.

16. In order to completely refute Tilak's interpretation in the *Taittirīya-Saṃhitā* and thus demolish his theory, Thibaut introduced the passage from the *Kauṣītaki-Brāhmaṇa* (XIX. 2, 3), and then stated that its references to the performance of the Sattra on the new moon day of different months of the year implied its late origin—as late as the *Jyotiṣa-Vedāṅga*; that the Cāturmāsya Sacrifice, dividing the year into 3-Seasons, pointed to the year beginning in warm season; that non-mention of the equinox by the ancient Indo-Aryans indicated their unfamiliarity with the same; that performance of the Sūtra on Ekāṣṭakā and 4 days before the full moon mentioned in the *Taittirīya-Saṃhitā* corroborated his supposition that the year beginning at a time much later than the Kṛttika-period was counted from solstice; and that all the four works—the *Taitt.*-Sam , the *Taṇḍya-Br., the Kauṣ-Br.* and the *Jyotiṣa-Vedāṅga*—were composed during this later period. Thibaut charged the ancient Indo-Aryans with 'looseness' of thinking, meaning thereby that no trust could be placed on their astronomical knowledge.

17, All these statements of Thibaut have been examined.

It has been shown that the passage from the *Kauṣītaki-Brāhmàṇa* does not contradict but support Tilak's interpretation of the passage from the *Taittirīya-Saṃhitā* used by him; that the references in the *Kauṣītaki Brāhmaṇa* to the performance of the Sattra on the new moon day in different months do not indicate as late origin of the two treatises as of the *Jyotiṣa-Vedāṅga*, but rather an earlier origin; that Cāturmāsya sacrifice had been unnecessarily introduced by Thibaut; that non-mention of equinox does not mean unfamiliarity of Indo-Aryans with the same; and that all evidences point to the correctness of Tilak's view regarding the antiquity of the *Ṛgveda*.

18. Till now, the approximate time of the composition of the different treatises—the *Taittirīya Saṃhitā*, the *Tāḍya Brāhmaṇa* and the *Kauṣītaki Brāḥmaṇa*—remained undecided. An attempt has been made here to place them in proper sequence of time. After a review of the opinions of the great scholars, one is now in a position to point out that in these ancient days the Indo-Aryans knew not only when to begin the year but also how to correct errors in year-counting whenever they arose. They distinguished one epoch from another by naming them after definite Nakṣatras, in consequence of which the present day scholars versed in Astronomy find it easier to indicate approximately the broad dates of happenings in Vedic times. Max Müller in his Introduction to the Texts of the *Ṛgveda*, edited by him, had completely demolished the idea of some eminent western scholars that the names of 27 Indian Nakṣatras were borrowed from elsewhere (Vol. 4, p.). It may therefore be stated without fear of contradiction that these 27 Nākṣatras held the key to the understanding of the age of the *Ṛgveda*. References in the *Brāhmaṇas* to Kṛttikās as the head of the Nakṣatras are really references to happenings in Kṛttikā epoch. Similarly, Mṛga (Śiras) in the *Ṛgveda* indicates the early Mṛgaśiras epoch, indicating 4000 B.C. as the date.

19. In my Presidential Address at the 19th Session of the Indian History Congress at Agra in 1956,[1] the date of Manu the first of the Indo-Aryan kings as 3966 or 4000 B.C. was arrived at in the following way approximately, whose sacrifices are mentioned in the Rv. The beginning of the reign of Candra Gupta Maurya in 322 B.C., and of 9 Nandas and 6 later Śiśunāgas from Bimbisāra to Mahānandin for 100 years and

1 See Indian Historical Quarterly, vol. No. 4, (Dec. 1956), Supplement.

169 years respectively are found recorded in history, the total number of years that passed between Bimbisara and the beginning of the Christian era is therefore 591. Prior to Bimbisāra, there were 125 kings viz. 4[1] undated or 5earlier Śiśunāgas, 5 Pradyotas, 22 Bṛhadrathas after Bhārata War, and 94 kings (including Manu, and excluding Abhimanyu who did not reign) before them.[2] No dated historical record is available about them, but of their names and in some cases their activities were memorised by a special class of people and handed down from generation to generation, in the form of Purāṇas. This historical tradition is much helpful in reconstructing the ancient history. In my Address, each of these kings has been allotted on the analogy of Toynbee 27 years on average, thus giving us 125 × 27 + 591 or 3966 years B.C. as the date of Manu.

20. The reason for accepting 27 on average as the length of reign for each king of historical tradition is that Toynbee in his "Study of History," Vol. X, p. 172, describes how more than ten eminent Western scholars, though differing widely in regard to the dates of the beginning and end of the First Babylonian Dynasty, agree that 11 kings reigned for 300 years, i.e. each king reigned for 27·27 years on average. ·27 years has been *drafted* and 27 years adopted as the average length of reign of left out Indo-Aryan king each.

21. Toynbee's average of 27·27 years' reign is in regard to the kings of the First Babylonian Dynasty. (Hammurabi etc.) He claims that this average is true for South-Western History. (*Ibid.*, p, 272). He is of opinion that "this would settle, within narrow limits, the dates of previous chapters of that history," which he calculated to be 2500 B. C. or earlier, for Toynbee gives the date of First Babylonian Dynasty as 1950-1651 B. C. The question now arises as to whether there is any justification in applying this average to the case of early Indian kings. The answer is in the affirmative. For, says he, "it was comparatively easy to *calculate* the Western civilization's chronology with the chronologies of its living contemporaries (the Near Eastern, Orthodox Christian, Russian Orthodox Christian, Iranic Muslim, Arabic Muslim, *Hindu*, Chinese Far Eastern, and Japanese Far Eastern Societies) and also with the

1 Four kings have been taken into account.

2 See The *Vedic Age*, Ed. by Dr. R. C. Majumder, Pusalkar's list of traditional kings in Chapter. , p.

See Dr. A.D. Pusalkar's see list of the aforesaid kings (taking p. 319) in the *Vedic Age*, Ed. by Dr R.C. Majumder·

chronologies of antecedent civilizations (the Hellenic, Syriac, *Indic* and Sinic). "Toynbee declares that the evidence in the possession of the western scholars was not enough to enable them to reconstruct with any degree of certainty the chronology of the earliest chapters in the histories even of those four civilizations belonging to a generation immediately preceding that of his own Society and its living contemporaries; and the uncertainty was greater still in the case of other civilizations...of whose history no continuous tradition has been preserved by any of the civilizations that were still alive in the twentieth century of the Christian era". (Ibid., pp. 167, 168). The uncertainty in the chronology of earliest chapters in the history of Indic or more aptly the ancient Indo-Aryan civilization, of which Toynbee speaks, is lessened by the continuous tradition preserved by the Purāṇas. Therefore that reconstruction is quite possible, and it has been attempted in the present thesis on literary and astronomical evidence.

96, Amherst Street,
Calcutta.

Narendranath Law

CONTENTS

CHAPTER 1

VIEWS OF SCHOLARS ON THE AGE OF THE ṚGVEDA

(2) VṚṢĀKAPI

(3) THE MANDUKAS

(FROGS)

(4) UPĀKARANA

(COMMENCEMENT OF THE STUDY OF THE VEDA IN EACH YEAR)

CHAPTER I

VIEWS OF SCHOLARS ON THE AGE OF THE ṚGVEDA

(*A*) *Max Müller's Divisions of the Vedic Period*

1. Max Müller (=M) (1823-1900) was the first scholar who tried in 1859 to construct a sort of chronology of the oldest Indian literature.[1] Alexander's invasion of India, and the appearance of Buddhism in the country are, according to him, the two fixed milestones, from which a start could be made of this chronology. As a reaction to Brahmanism, Buddhism presupposes the existence of the Veda with the Hymns, Brāhmaṇas, Āraṇyakas, and Upaniṣads, which must, therefore, be dated before 600 B.C. He fixes the time for the Sūtra literature as 600 to 200 B.C., and allots 200 years to each of the three periods for Chandas, Mantra, and Brāhmaṇa, that precede the Sūtra period. So, the first three periods of ancient Vedic literature may be arranged in the following manner:

Max Müller's allotment of 200 years to each stratum of Vedic literature results in landing us in 1200 B. C. or 1500 B. C. as the time of origin of the *Ṛgveda*.

1. 1200 to 1000 B.C.—Chandas
2. 1000 to 800 B.C.—Mantra
3. 800 to 600 B.C.—Brāhmaṇa

2. The earliest times which produced poetry of the ancient Ṛṣis constituted the Chandas period. While referring to whatever is left of the language and poetry of that period, M. speaks of their charm as unsurpassed by Indian literature of any later age. He characterizes this poetry as beautiful, original, and spontaneous.[2] The greater portion of the *Ṛgveda* belongs to the Mantra period, which succeeded the Chandas. The hymns uttered then were expressions of the spontaneous impulses of the human heart.[3]

The different periods of Vedic literature and their characteristics. The Chandas Period.

1 Max Müller, *History of Ancient Sanskrit Literature* (=*History*) (1859), Pāṇini ES., p. 295. Winternitz gives a summary of M's arguments in his *History of Indian Literature*, vol. I, p. 292.

Cf. also Max Müller, *Preface to the Ṛgveda Saṃhitā* (Text), (1862), vol. IV, pp. v-vii

2 Max Müller, *History*, p. 271. Elsewhere in the *Preface to the Ṛgveda Saṃhitā* (Text), vol. IV, p. vii, M. writes of the "ancient poets or Rishis, who, by their songs, gave the first impulse to the religion, the poetry, the worship of the Aryan dwellers in India."

3 Max Müller, *History*, p. 271

3(a). M. cites several instances of hymns, belonging to the Chandas period[1]. Extracts from three of them are given below to explain their nature.

Hymn VII. 77

She shines upon us, like a young wife, rousing every living being to go to his work. The fire had to be kindled by men ; she brought light by striking down darkness.—*Ṛk* 1.

Shine for us with thy best rays, thou bright Dawn, thou who lengthenest our life, thou the love of all, who givest us food, who givest us wealth in cows, horses, and chariots[2].—*Ṛk* 5.

Hymn VII. 86

Wise and mighty are the works of him (Varuṇa) who stemmed asunder the wide firmaments. He lifted on high the bright and glorious heaven; he stretched out apart the starry sky and the earth[3].—*Ṛk* 1.

Hymn VII. 89

Let me not yet, O Varuṇa, enter into the house of clay; have mercy, Almighty, have mercy !—*Ṛk* 1.

If I go along trembling, like a cloud driven by the wind, have mercy, Almighty, have mercy[4].—*Ṛk* 2.

1 For the hymns, see Max Müller, *op. cit.*, pp. 274 ff.

2 Max Müller, *op. cit.*, p. 284 ; Text, vol. IV :

उपो रुरुचे युवतिर्न योषा विश्वं जीवं प्रसुवन्ती चरायै ।

अभूदग्निः समिधे मानुषाणामकर्ज्योतिर्बाधमाना तमांसि ॥७,७७,१॥

p. 187

अस्मे श्रेष्ठेभिर्भानुभिर्वि भाह्युषो देवि प्रतिरन्ती न आयुः ।

इषं च नो दधती विश्ववारे गोमदश्वावद्रथवच्च राधः ॥७,७७,५॥

p. 189

Cf. H. H. Wilson's Tr. of the *Ṛgveda Saṃhitā*, vol IV, pp. 160, 161

3 Max Müller, *op. cit.*, p. 279 ; Tex, vol. IV :

धीरा त्वस्य महिना जनूंषि वि यस्तस्तम्भ रोदसी चिदुर्वी ।

प्र नाकमृष्वं नुनुदे बृहन्तं द्विता नक्षत्रं पप्रथच्च भूम ॥७,८६,१॥

p. 212

Max Müller, *op. cit.*, p. 278 ; Text, vol. IV :

मो षु वरुण मृन्मयं गृहं राजन्नहं गमम् ।

मृळा सुक्षत्र मृळय ॥७,८९,१॥

यदेमि प्रस्फुरन्निव दृतिर्न ध्मातो अद्रिवः ।

मृळा सुक्षत्र मृळय ॥२॥

pp, 222, 223

Regarding the hymn to Dawn, M. speaks of it as a fair specimen of the simple and original poetry of the Veda. It has no reference to any sacrifice, it can hardly be called a hymn in the usual sense of the word[1].

3(b). The Chandas period was followed by the Mantra period. Mantra is the name of a hymn employed for sacrificial purposes.[2]

The Mantra Period

The literature of the Brāhmaṇa period exhibits a stratum of thought, which is unintelligible without the admission of a preceding age, during which the diverse features of the *Brāhmaṇas* had their natural growth, their meaning and purpose[3].

The only document available for the study of the character of the Mantra literature is the *Ṛgveda Saṃhitā.*

In describing the time when the collection of the hymns of the *Ṛgveda* took place, M. agrees with Roth that it was "a less practical age than that of the Brāhmaṇa period ; an age, not entirely free from the trammels of a ceremonial, yet not completely enslaved by a system of mere formalities ; an age no longer creative and impulsive, yet not without some power of upholding the traditions of a past that spoke to a later generation of men through the very poems which they were collecting with so much zeal and accuracy."[4]

There is ample internal evidence in the hymns themselves that some of their authors belong to a later generation. Hence a distinction must be made between the primitive (Chandas), and the secondary (Mantra) period. That the later hymns are not the outcome of a free, original, and unconscious inspiration is only natural[5].

(1) May I never go, royal Varuṇa, to a house made of clay: grant me happiness, possessor of wealth, grant me happiness.

(2) When, Varuṇa, I am throbbing as if (with awe) like an inflated skin, grant me happiness, possessor of wealth, grant me happiness.

Wilson, Tr., vol IV, p. 180

1 Max Müller *History*, p. 278. He remarks that the language of the simple prayers of the Chandas period is "more intelligible to us, their whole world of thought and feeling is nearer to us, than anything we find in the literature of Greece and Rome, and there are, here and there, short expressions of faith and devotion, in which even a Christian can join without irreverence."

2 Max Müller, *Preface to the Ṛgveda Saṃhitā*, vol. IV, p. vi

3 Max Müller, *History*, p. 236

4 *I bid*, p. 246

5 *Ibid.*, p. 256

The Brāhmaṇa Period.

3(c). The orthodox view regarding the Veda is that the Veda-Saṃhitā is divided into two parts.[1] Mantra and Brāhmaṇa together are called the Veda. They are closely connected. For this reason, M. remarks that "whatever does not come under the name of Mantra is Brāhmaṇa, whether it contains reasons, explanations, answers, censures, recommendations, doubts, commandments, relations, old stories, or particular determinations.[2] The Brāhmaṇas profess to teach the performance of the sacrifice, but additional materials, explanations, illustrations, etc. of things connected with the original faith and ceremonial, occupy large portions of the Brāhmaṇas[3]. They are mostly in prose.

The Brāhmaṇas are a broad division of the Vedic literature comprising Brāhmaṇa proper, Āraṇyaka, and Upaniṣad.

Brāhmaṇa proper.

The Brāhmaṇa proper is the *Karma-Kāṇḍa* (rituals) of the Veda. To dilate on the meaning and application of particular Mantras is its main purpose.

Āraṇyaka.

The second portion is called the Āraṇyaka. It serves as a bridge between rituals and spiritual knowledge. It had to be studied by a Brahmacārin (student) during his stay at the residence of his Guru in the first *āśrama* (the first stage of life). At the time of reading the Āraṇyakas, a sequestered place, whence no roofs of tenements were visible,[4] or a forest outside the village[5], had to be selected for the purpose. Until the Āraṇyakas were finished, the studies were not considered to be completed. As it was the practice to study the Āraṇyakas in forest, they were called the 'forest portion' of the Brāhmaṇa[6]. Sacrifices

1 मन्त्रब्राह्मणयो र्वेदनामधेयम् ।
Āpastamba-Yājñaparibhāṣā-Sūtra, I. 33

2 Max Müller, *History*, p. 176

3 *Ibid.*, p. 175

4 At the time of reciting Mantras in Āraṇyaka-vrata named Śukriya, one had to go to अच्छदिर्दर्श region.

अध्येष्यमाणः प्राचीमुदीचीं दिशमुपनिष्क्रम्य देशेऽच्छदिर्दर्शे पराचीनमधीयीत ।
Āpastamba-Śrauta-Sūtra, 21. 3 & 10

5 अपि वारण्ये तिष्ठेदास्तमयात् । *Gobhla-Gṛhya-Sūtra*, 3. 2. 33 शुक्लपक्षे वहिर्ग्रामाद्विविक्तं देशमेत्य वा ॥ *Āśvalāyana-Gṛhya-Kārikā*, 14. 3

6 ऐतरेयब्राह्मणेऽस्ति काण्डमारण्यकाभिधम् । अरण्य एव पाठ्यत्वादारण्यकमितीर्यते । [The name of one of the Kāṇḍas is Āraṇyaka. As it had to be read in forest, it was so called.]

have been expressly mentioned in the Āraṇyakas, but they were practised as mental operations without the external paraphernalia.

The Brahmacārin after returning home at the end of his studies at the residence of his Guru became a householder (Gṛhin). During that period the lessons taught by his Guru from the Āraṇyakas were cogitated by him at intervals in a secluded place. When after the age of fifty, he went out to live in a forest in the third stage of life (Vānaprastha), he was not in a position to perform sacrifices due to his inability to collect the requisites for the same. He performed the rituals mentally according to the Āraṇyakas for spiritual progress[1].

The third portion of the Brāhmaṇa is called the Upaniṣad. It is, in fact, a collection of chapters on philosophy. There are passages in the Āraṇyakas and Upaniṣads "unequalled in any language for grandeur, boldness, and simplicity".[2]

Upaniṣad.

The vastness of the prose literature in the Brāhmaṇas and its gradual evolution requiring a long period can be imagined from what has been said already in this para.

3(d). M. places last the Sūtra period allotting to it 400 years from 600 B. C. to 200 B. C. The strictly orthodox view does not include the Sūtras in the Vedas (Śruti), which, according to that view, close with Upaniṣad.

The Sūtra Period.

Sūtra means string ; and all the works written in this style are nothing but one uninterrupted string of short sentences[3].

They are manuals containing specific procedural directions for performing the sacrifices, which were gradually increasing in bulk. The desultory discussions of the procedure (Kalpa) described in the Brāhmaṇas could not be used as practical guides. For this reason, the composition of the Sūtras became necessary.

(*B*) *Criticisms on 200-year period for each Vedic stratum*

4. The fixation of 200 years as the time for the formation of each stratum of Vedic literature led many to deny its antiquity. M. was opposed by several scholars such as H. H. Wilson, B. Saint-Hilaire, and W. D. Whitney. In his *Preface* to the 4th vol.

1 Some information regarding the Āraṇyakas has been taken from a pamphlet by Prof. Durga Mohan Bhattacharyya.

2 Max Müller, *History*, p. 174

3 *Ibid.*, p. 36

of the *Ṛgveda Saṃhita* (Text) (1862), M. quoted *in extenso* the remarks of these scholars, and tried to meet them.

Extracts from Wilson's remarks as quoted by M. from the *Edinburgh Review*, 1860, p. 375, are given below :

Wilson is in favour of making each stratum as long as 500 years.

"Professor Müller thinks it impossible to assign a shorter interval than two centuries for the origin and accumulation of the mass of Brahmanical literature that must have existed. We confess that we are disposed to look upon this limit as much too brief for the establishment of an elaborate ritual, for the appropriation of all spiritual authority by the Brahmans, for the distinction of races or the institution of caste, and for the mysticism and speculation of the Āraṇyakas or Upanishads: a period of five centuries would not seem to be too protracted for such a complete remodelling of the primitive system and its wide dissemination through all those parts of India where the Brahmans have spread."

"[We] think there can be little doubt that, instead of two centuries, we may venture to conjecture four or five, and so carry the commencement of the Brahmaṇa period to the tenth or eleventh century B.C."[1]

Max Müller modifies a little his previous opinion about years to be allotted to each Vedic stratum.

5. Such criticisms *served to give a turn to M's opinion*, which can be traced to 1862. For, in the above-mentioned *Preface*, he declares: "I need hardly say that I agree with almost every word of my critics. I have repeatedly dwelt on the merely hypothetical character of the dates, which I ventured to assign to the first three periods of Vedic literature. *All I have claimed for them has been that they are minimum dates*, and that the literary productions of each period which either still exist or which formerly existed, could hardly be accounted for within shorter limits of time than those suggested."[2]

Like many other scholars, he also felt that 200 years were scarcely sufficient to account for the growth of the poetic literature ascribed to the Chandas period.[3]

He states that it was pointed out to him "that although on the evidence of literature alone, no higher antiquity could

1 Max Müller, *Praface to the Ṛgveda Saṃhitā* (Text), vol. IV, p. viii. Wilson's further remarks will be found in para 6 (b).

2 Max Müller, *Preface to the Ṛgveda Saṃhitā* (Text), vol. IV, p. xiii

3 *Ibid.*, p. xiii

have been claimed for the earliest poetry of India than the thirteenth century B. C., I ought to have strengthened my argument by additional evidence, and particularly by that of certain astronomical data which have long been brought forward as establishing the existence of Vedic poetry as early as the fifteenth century B. C."[1]

6. Since the publication of the above opinion of M., there appeared other observations on his theory.

Martin Haug places the commencement of Vedic literature in 2400-2000 B.C.

6(a). In 1863, in his *Preface* to the edition of the Text of the *Aitareya Brāhmaṇa,* Martin Haug puts the date of the composition of the bulk of the *Brāhmaṇas* between 1400 and 1200 B.C. A period of *at least* 500 to 600 years is, in his opinion, necessary for the Saṃhitā, with an interval of 200 years between the end of the Saṃhitā, and the beginning of the Brāhmaṇa proper. "Thus," says he, "we obtain for the bulk of the Saṃhitā the space from 1400-2000 B, C.; the oldest hymns and sacrificial formulas may be a few hundred years more ancient still, so that we would fix the very commencement of Vedic Literature between 2400-2000 B.C."[2] Thus, 2400 to 2000 B.C. is fixed for the commencement of the Vedic literature ; 2000 to 1400 B.C. for the composition of the bulk of the *Saṃhitā* ; and 1400 to 1200 B.C. for the composition of the bulk of the *Brāhmaṇas.*

Wilson's view as to the date of composition of the earliest Vedic works.

6(b). In addition to what Wilson wrote in the *Edinburgh Review,* he further remarked in his *Introduction* to his English translation of the *Ṛgveda Saṃhitā,* that many of the historical and genealogical traditions contained in the *Rāmāyaṇa, Mahābhārata, Purāṇas* etc. had foundations in fact, So, "the course of events, the extension of Hindus through India, the origin and succession of regal dynasties, and the formation of powerful principalities, all unknown to the *Sanhitā,* are equally indicative of the lapse of centuries between the composition of the *Sūktas* and the date of the earliest works that are subsequent to the great religious, social, and political

1 *Ibid.*, p. xiv

2 M. Haug, *Aitareya Brāhmaṇa of the Ṛgveda,* vol. I (1863), Intro., pp. 47, 48

changes which, in the interval, had taken place".[1] The interval is estimated by him to have been more than 1000 years.[2]

According to Jacobi, 1500 B.C. or thereabout is an impossible date regarding the composition of the *Ṛgveda.*

6(c). Jacobi (=J) refers[3] to M's assumption of a minimum of 200 years for each of the last three out of his four Vedic strata. He states: "This estimate is far below the minimum of the possible period, during which in India a department of literature could take its rise, reach perfection, become obsolete and die out, to give place finally to a thoroughly new departure. For a Brāhmaṇa, for example, could not be widely spread by being learned by heart by a gradually extending circle of Brahmans, and with the size of the country, this would certainly demand a long time. Every man, who learned such a work, became, so to say, a copy of it, and to carry out the figure, a written copy, to which no new work could be added. But several of such works must successively take the place of their predecessors, before the entire class of works in question became obsolete. I maintain that a minimum of a thousand years must rather be taken for such a process, which in the conditions that prevailed in ancient India was of necessity a very slow one, especially when we take into consideration that in historical times the literature of the classical period remained for more than a thousand years nearly unaltered".[4]

Tilak holds the view that many centuries had elapsed before human mind could grow so luxuriant as to accelerate the development of literature within a short period.

6(d). In regard to M's division of the Vedic literature into 4 periods—the Chandas, Mantra, Brāhmaṇa, and Sūtra,—Tilak (=T) remarks in his *Orion*: "As each period presupposes the preceding, while the last or the Sūtra period is prior, 'if not to the origin, but at least,' to the spreading and political ascendency of Buddhism in the fourth century before Christ, that learned scholar (i.e. M.), by assigning two hundred years for each period arrives at about 1200 B.C. *as the latest date,* at which we may suppose the Vedic hymns to have been composed."[5]

1 Wilson, *Introduction* to his translation of the *Ṛgveda Saṃhitā,* vol. I, First Aṣṭaka (2nd ed. 1866), p. xlv

2 Ibid., xlvi

3 *Indian Antiquary* (=*IA*), "On the Date of the Ṛgveda" by H. G. Jacobi (translated from the German by J. Morison), June, 1894, vol. 23, pp. 154-159

4 *Ibid.*, p. 158

5 B. G. Tilak, *Orion or Researches into the Antiquity of the Vedas* (Poona, 1893), p. 2

T. points out that there are different opinions as to the divisions of the Vedic literature, some holding that the Chandas and Mantra cover one period, though a long one.[1]

In this connection, T. cites Haug's calculations for the commencement of the Vedic literature between 2400 and 2000 B.C. and says that the assumption of each period being 200 years (M.), 500 years (Haug and Wilson), or 1000 years cannot help us to arrive at the age of the Veda, and that other means must be found out for the purpose.[2] The other means referred to is astronomical calculation.

Oldest Vedic hymns cannot be placed in 1500 B. C. (Bühler).

6 (e). Bühler (=B.) supports[3] J's opinion that the assignment of 200 years by M. to the development of each of the three oldest forms of Vedic composition leads to sheer impossibilities, and that materials from Indian literature itself supply general and special arguments for the objection. The stage, says he, which the Indo-Aryan researches had reached rules out altogether the placing of the oldest Vedic hymns at about 1200 or even 1500 B.C. He does not support M's supposition that the early literary activities of India showed greater luxuriance[4] than that of later periods, and hence "the conjecture that the ancient Indo-Aryans raced through the so-called Chhndas, Mantra, and Brāhmaṇa periods at a furiously fast pace, loses its chief support".[5]

(C) *Evidence of Max Müller's far-reaching change of opinion at the end*

7. In one of the series of Hibbert Lectures delivered by M. on the *Origin and Growth of Religion*[6], he is seen to be still holding the theory regarding the age of the *Ṛgveda* as enunciated by him in his *History of Ancient Sanskrit Literature*,[7] though he seemed to modify it in 1862. Even then his idea was that "there is

Max Müller's views in the Hibbert Lectures (1878).

1 *Ibid.*, p. 3

2 *Ibid.*, p. 4

3 *IA.*, Sept., 1894, vol. 23, pp. 238-249: "Note on Professor Jacobi's Age of the Veda and on Professor Tilak's Orion" by G. Bühlcr.

4 In his *Preface to the Ṛgveda Saṃhitā* (Text), vol. IV, p. vii, M. states that the limit of 200 years can be assigned to each period "only under the supposition that, during the early periods of history, the growth of the human mind was more luxuriant than in later times."

5 *IA.*, p. 246

6 Delivered at the Chapter House, Westminister Abbey, in April, May and June, 1878

7 See pp. 153-156

nothing more ancient and primitive, not only in India, but in the whole Aryan world, than the hymns of the *Rigveda.* So far as we are Aryans in language, that is in thought, so far the *Rig-veda* is our own most ancient book."[1] In other words, he could not think of any earlier date at that time.

Max Müller's opinion undergoes a very great change in his Gifford Lectures (1890).

8. All this changed when M. spoke on *Physical Religion* in his *Gifford Lectures* in 1890. There are many passages in them which leave no doubt as to what really was M's idea regarding the antiquity of the *Ṛgveda.* Some of the passages are given below:

(a) "........it (*Rigveda*) is more primitive than any other literary work we are acquainted with."[2]

(b) "......We possess in the whole world no literary relics intellectually older than the oldest hymns of the *Rig-veda,* and I doubt whether we possess any literary relics chronologically older at all events, in our own, the Aryan world."[3]

(c) "......Who can deny that Veda (*Rigveda*) is the oldest monument of Aryan speech and Aryan thought, which we possess?"[4]

(d) "......We do find there (in the *Rigveda*), and there alone, the oldest record of what one branch of that race thought about this life and its many problems and what is believed about the gods and another life."[5]

(e) "If now we ask how we can fix the date of these three periods, it is quite clear that we cannot hope to fix a *terminum a quo.* Whether the Vedic hymns were composed 1000, or 1500, or 2000, or 3000 years B. C. no power on earth will ever determine."[6]

9. Two facts may be mentioned here to show that M. was quite conscious of his first estimate of the age of the *Ṛgveda* falling short of what it should have been.

(a) In the *Preface* to his *Arctic Home in the Vedas* (1903)[7], T. refers to the different strata into which Vedic literature was

1 Hibbert Lectures, p. 157
2 Max Müller, Collected Works, vol. 2, *Physical Religion* (1890), p. 14
3 *Ibid.*, pp. 14, 15
4 *Ibid.*, p. 17
5 *Ibid.*, p. 20
6 *Ibid.*, p. 91
7 According to Tilak's statement, the first manuscript of the book was written at the end of 1898 (p. iv).

Max Müller's sympathetic views on the summary of Tilak's Book (1903).

divided and the times allotted to them. Before the publication of the *Orion* in 1893, it was generally believed that the oldest of the strata could not be older than 2400 B.C.[1] He tried to show in the *Orion* that there are astronomical data in the *Ṛgveda* and other Vedic literature, which supply reliable evidence for ascertaining the different periods of Vedic literature, and that these astronomical statements "unmistakably pointed out that the Vernal equinox was in the constellation of Mṛiga or Orion (about 4500 B.C.) during the period of the Vedic hymns, and that it had receded to the constellation of the Kṛittikās, or the Pleiades (about 2500 B.C.) in the days of the Brāhmaṇas."[2]

Though this theory was received by some scholars with doubts yet the force of the arguments was acknowledged by Jacobi, Bloomfield, Barth, Bühler, Dikshit and others. Bloomfield, in an Address on the occasion of the 18th anniversary of John Hopkins University, referred to Tilak's book the *Orion* and expressed the opinion that "the language and literature of the Vedas is, by no means, so primitive as to place with it the real beginnings of Aryan life", which may reach back, according to him, several thousands of years more.[3]

These words encouraged T. in his researches regarding the primitive home of the Aryans, in which he was engaged for the last ten years (1893-1903). Relying on Vedic evidence, he wrote down his first manuscript at the end of 1898, and *sent a brief summary* to M. In it he modified his theory as expressed in the *Orion* (1893). He divided the period from the commencement of post-Glacial era to the birth of Buddha into five divisions. Of these, we are concerned with the following:

(1) 5000 to 3000 B. C.—Orion (i. e. the asterism Mṛgaśiras) period, when the vernal equinox was in the Orion. Many Vedic hymns were traced by T. to this period.

1 "The chief result of my inquiry would be evident from the title of the essay. The high antiquity of the Egyptian civilization is now generally admitted. But scholars still hesitate to place the commencement of the Vedic civilization earlier than 2400 B. C. I have endeavoured to show in the following pages that the traditions recorded in the *Rigveda* unmistakably point to a period *not later* than 4000 B. C., when the vernal equinox was in Orion, or, in other words, when the Dog-star (or the Dog as we have it in the *Rigveda*), commenced the equinoctial year." Preface to *Orion*, p. iii

2 B. G. Tilak, *Arctic Home in the Vedaș* (1903), Preface, p. i

3 *Ibid.*, p. ii

(2) 3000 to 1400 B.C,—Kṛttikā i. e. the asterism Pleiades period.[1]

The main point sought to be established in the *Arctic Home* may be given briefly in T's own words as follows: "......the beginnings of Aryan civilisation must be supposed to date back several thousand years before the oldest Vedic period ; and when the commencement of the Post-glacial epoch is brought down to 8000 B.C., it is not at all surprising if the date of primitive Aryan life is found to go back to it from 4500 B.C., the age of the oldest Vedic period."[2]

It may be mentioned that to arrive at the above conclusion, T. used 542 passages from the *Ṛgveda* (the number of Sūktas being of course much less). In regard to 77 of these passages, his interpretations, he mentions, were different from those of Yāska and Sāyaṇa, and thereby their obscurity was removed.[3]

T. did not expect that "a scholar, who had worked all his life on a different line, would accept the view[4] at once, and that too on reading a bare outline of the evidence in its support. Still it was encouraging to hear from him that though the interpretations of Vedic passages proposed by me were probable, yet my theory appeared to be in conflict with the established geological facts."[5]

T. replied that he would soon place before M. elaborately the evidence that supported his view, but unfortunately, M. died (in 1900) before this could be done.[6]

9 (b). M. Winternitz deals with the age of the *Ṛgveda* in his *History of Indian Literature* and tries to give an explanation of M's theory in the following way:[7]

What M. did was nothing more than the fixing of the lowest limit. Winternitz considers that the placing of the *Ṛgveda* between

1 *Ibid.*, p. 454

2 *Ibid.*, p. vi

3 *Ibid.*, p. vi. See Index of Vedic passages (used by T.), pp. 491-500.

4 The view is that the Aryans had originally an Arctic Home and that the Mṛgaśiras, and Kṛttikā periods began 5000 B. C., and 3000 B. C. respectively.

5 *Ibid.*, pp. iii, iv. T. thanked M. for his disinterested kindness in getting him free from prison earlier than the fixed term (18 months,—reduced to 12) through the efforts of M. and many friends, and on this occasion, he sent the summary mentioned above.

6 *Ibid.*, p. iv

7 M. Winternitz, *A History of Indian Literature* (English translation), vol. 1 (1927). The original German book had been published about 20 years ago (about 1907).

Winternitz's explanation of Max Müller's aforesaid theory.

1200 B. C. and 1000 B. C. is hypothetical and arbitrary, and regrets that this notion "in the course of years, received more and more the dignity and character of a scientifically proved fact."[1]

Winternitz asks for a more liberal interpetation of M's statement, because M. himself did not mean that the interval of 200 years for each period really took place, and that in 1000 B. C. *at the latest the Ṛgveda Saṃhitā* was completed.[2] He considered 1200 to 1000 B. C. only as the lowest limit. Winternitz then refers to the passage quoted already[3] from Gifford Lectures to prove his own thesis.

(D) *Duration of each Vedic stratum*

10 (a). Inadequacy of a period of 200 years for each stratum of Vedic literature may also be evident by the consideration of the following facts.

That by 1200 B. C. or even 1500 B. C. the greater portion of India should be Aryanized is regarded as an impossibility by B.

Aryanization of large portions of India could not have been accomplished by 1500 B. C.

He cannot also accept the view that the ancient Indo-Aryans acquired such a large area, and founded different states within the space of five to eight hundred years. It should also be borne in mind that this area had been inhabited not only by forest tribes but also by people possessing a civilization not much inferior to that of the invaders. For these reasons, even double of the period of 800 years mentioned above might not have been sufficient for the purpose.[4]

The existence of the heterodox sect (Jainism) in the latter half of the 8th century B.C. makes the beginning of the Brāhmaṇa period in 800 B. C. an impossibility.

10 (b). B. points out that researches on religious history show that the number of religions that appeared as a protest against Hinduism and in defiance of the authority of the Vedas was more than one.

Of the heterodox sects, Jainism is one, and its founder Pārśva[5] stated to have died in B. C. 776. B. remarks that if it be admitted

1 M. Winternitz, *History*, vol. I, p. 293

2 *Ibid.*, p. 293

3 See para 8(e).

4 *IA.*, 1894, p. 247

5 According to Jacobi, he was the real founder of Jainism, and lived in the second half of the 8th century B. C.

that a sect, whose teachings are based on the doctrine of Jñāna-mārga, sprang up at that early period, it becomes impossible to reconcile this admission with the theory that the Brāhmaṇa period began in 800 B. C.

B. refers to another heterodox sect called Bhāgavata, or Sātvata, or Pāñcarātra as much anterior to the rise of Jainism. He states that "still more irreconcilable with the theory that the literary activity of the Indo-Aryans began about 1200 or 1500 B. C. is another point, which, I think, can be proved, viz. that the ancient Bhāgavata, Sātvata, or Pāñcarātra sect, devoted to the worship of Nārāyaṇa and its deified teacher Kṛishṇa Devakīputra, dates from a period long anterior to the rise of the Jainas in the eighth century B. C. To give the details here would unduly lengthen this already long note. And I reserve their discussion for my *Indian Studies*, No. IV."[1]

As the Bhāgavata sect is anterior to Jainism, it is impossible to fix the date of early Aryan literary activities at 1500 B. C.

11. On both the counts, Winternitz gives partial support to B.

(1) In regard to the Aryanization, B. states that the growth and development of the *Ṛgveda* and Vedic literature taught by generations of teachers took several centuries, and that during this long period the Aryans did not advance beyond the stretch of land between the Indus and the Ganges. Thereafter he asks: If this advance from the extreme north-west to the eastern Gangetic land occupied such long time, how many centuries then must have been necessary for bringing into fold the whole of central and southern India. His answer is that in view of the above circumstances 700 years (1500 B. C. to 800 B. C.) will not appear to be a very long period.[2]

Aryanization of the country not possible by 1500 B. C.—
(i) because of the vastness of its area ;

(ii) B's statement that Buddhism and other early heterodox sects in India presuppose the completion of the whole of the Vedic literature is supported by Winternitz. He endorses the opinion of Oldenberg as against that of Hopkins, Rapson and others that many centuries must have elapsed between the earliest Upaniṣads and earliest heterodox literature. If Jaina and Bhāgavata literature be taken to have filled the intervening period, the date of the Upaniṣads, the Āraṇyakas, the Brāhmaṇas, and

(ii) because of the completion of the Vedic literature before the rise of heterodox sects.

1 *IA.*, 1894, p. 248

2 M. Winternitz, *History*, vol. 1, pp. 300-303

consequently Mantras, and Chandas, must be pushed back further. As the development of the whole of the great Vedic literature cannot be explained, if it be dated in 1500 B. C., he points to about 2000 B. C. or 2500 B. C. as the commencement of the said literature.

The possibility of some deities at Boghaz Köi being Vedic Indian gods pushes back the date of the *Ṛgveda* to nearly 2000 B. C.

12. Among the documents found by Hugo Winckler in the excavations at Bogh'az Köi (Asia Minor) in 1907, some Hittite clay tablets were discovered recording treaties between Subbiluliuma, the king of the Hittites, and Mattiurja, the king of Mitani, dated about 1400 B. C. The deities of both the nations are invoked as guardians of the treaties. The names of Mitra, Varuṇa, Indra, and Nāsatyas (i. e. the two Aśvins) are found among the Mitani deities.

Ilāni *mi-it-ra*-aš-ši-il ilāni
uru-w-na-aš-ši-el
(Variant) *a-ru-na*-aš-ši-il
ilu *in-dar* ilāni *nā-ša-a* [*t-ti-ia-a*)-n-na
(Variant) *in-da-ra* nā-š [a]-*at-ti-ia*-an-na[1]

The discovery of the five Indian gods caused some perplexity among the scholars, specially because the names were grouped together in the same way as in the *Ṛgveda*. J. states that the two groupings establish the Vedic origin and character of the deities which were adopted into the Mitani pantheon. For this reason, any suggestion pointing to date the *Ṛgveda* later than about 1400 B. C. is an impossibility.[2]

This view is accepted by Sten Konow, Hillerbrandt, and Winternitz. For the explanation of the association of the Vedic deities with those of Mitani, Winternitz remarks that an assumption is necessary that just as there had been immigration of the Aryans into India from the West, so there must have been isolated migrations of the Aryans from India to the West.

1 *JRAS*., 1909, "On the Antiquity of Vedic Culture", by H.Jacobi, p. 723
2 Winternitz, *History*, vol. i. pp. 304-306

CHAPTER 2

ASTRONOMICAL EVIDENCE ON THE AGE OF THE ṚGVEDA

13. Scholars have attempted to establish the age of the Ṛgveda with the help of astronomical evidence, collected from the *Ṛgveda* and other Vedic literature. In interpreting the same texts, they have differed, rendering the ultimate conclusions different. An attempt will be made here to see how far they agree or differ in regard to some conclusions from textual and astronomical data and whether any dependable results can emerge.

Difference of opinion as to the conclusions from astronomical evidence.

Winternitz remarks in this connection that "Attempts to determine the period of the Veda by the aid of *astronomy* come to grief owing to the fact that there are certain passages in the Vedic texts which admit of various interpretations. However correct the astronomical calculations may be, they prove nothing unless the texts in question admit of an unambigous interpretation."[1]

T., however, uses astronomical evidence in his *Orion* (1893) in which he states that "a comparison with Bentley's work will show that the present essay is more literary than astronomical in its character. In other words, it is the Sanskrit scholars who have first of all to decide if my interpretations of certain texts are correct, and when this judgment is once given, it is not at all difficult to astronomically calculate the exact period of the traditions in the Rigveda."[2]

14. T. in 1893, and J. in 1894, published almost identical results of their astronomical investigations into the age of the *Ṛgveda*, carried on independently of each other.[3] T. calls the period from 5000 B. C. to 3000 B. C. the Orion Period,[4] as during these 2000 years, the vernal equinox passed gradually from the commencement of the asterism Orion (Mṛgaśiras) to that of the next,

Tilak and Jacobi's conclusions agree, and are supported by Bühler.

1 Winternitz, *History*, p. 30.

2 Preface to the *Orion*, p. v

3 See T's *Orion* (1893), as also J's article "On the Date of the Rigveda" in *IA*., June, 1894, vol. 23, pp. 154-159.

4 In 1893 in the *Orion*, T. had stated that the Orion Period lasted from 4000 B.C. to 2500 B.C., which was strongly opposed by Whitney, and Thibaut in *IA*., 1895. He, however, followed his own line of thought, and considered it fit later on to fix the Orion Period as 5000 B.C. to 3000 B.C. in the *Arctic Home* (1903), p. 454.

viz. Pleiades (Kṛttikās). Many hymns of the *Ṛgveda* (including the Vṛṣākapi hymn) were in existence at that time.

According to J., the period of Vedic civilisation extended from 4500 B.C. to 2500 B.C.[1]

Both the scholars, J. and T., turned to B. independently of each other for his opinion. In an article, entitled "Note on Professor Jacobi's Age of the Veda and Professor Tilak's *Orion*" in the *IA.*, 1894, pp. 238-249, B. declared that both of them had made good their main proposition, viz. that the Kṛttikā-series is not the oldest Nakṣatra series known to the Hindus, but that they knew of another preceding it viz. the Mṛgaśiras-series.

I shall have occasion to discuss more fully the opinions of J, and T. and their criticisms by Whitney (=W.)[2] and Thibaut[3] (=Th.) and the support received by them from B. Only a brief statement of the position has been given above.

15. W. and Th.'s criticisms of J. and T. require very careful scrutiny. It should be stated at the outset that the exactitude of modern astronomers helped by present-day instruments cannot be expected from the ancient investigators in the field of astronomy.

Whitney and Thibaut hold views opposite to those of Jacobi and Tilak.

Nor do J. and T. claim it, All that is expected is that the ancient astronomers should be judged by the standard that prevailed in those times. Their main props were observation, and more observation. They had to be very careful in this matter, for they knew that an inaccuracy unchecked long would vitiate their activities, secular as well as religious, including the performance of the sacrifices. Therefore, they had to be well-acquainted with the Nakṣatras, the courses of the sun and moon, the proper length of the year, months etc. There is no reason to believe that they were completely devoid of astronomical knowledge or that they allowed a mistake to continue for any length of time. We owe it to J., T., and B. that they have removed many unfounded notions regarding the astronomy of ancient Indians.

1 *IA.*, June, 1894, p. 157

2 Whitney's article is entitled "On a recent Attempt, by Jacobi and Tilak, to determine on Astronomical Evidence the Date of the Earliest Vedic Period as 4000 B.C.". It was first published in the Proceedings of the American Oriental Society, March, 1894, and reprinted after his death in *IA.*, 1895, pp. 361-369.

3 Thibaut's article "On some recent Attempts to determine the Antiquity of Vedic civilization," appeared in *IA.*, April, 1895, pp. 85-100.

A careful study of the opinions of Jacobi and Tilak with the supporting evidence is necessary.

16. I want to mention in this connection that though more than sixty years have passed since J. and T. wrote and were adversely criticised by W. and Th. and were supported by B, the views expressed by them did not receive the attention they deserved.

Difficulty in properly interpreting Vedic texts.

17. One difficulty in studying the texts used by different scholars for determining the age of the Veda lies in the fact that after the lapse of so many centuries, the old traditions having been lost, it taxes the brain to the utmost at times, to find out the right interpretation of Vedic texts. Couched as many of them are in language through which it is difficult to get at the real meaning, even Yāska or Sāyaṇa's comments do not reach the fullest clarity. For this reason, every Vedic scholar has to fall back upon his own intelligence to interpret a passage or solve a problem connected with the same.

(1) THE ṚBHUS

(SEASONS)

18. I shall now proceed to examine some of the opinions advanced by J. and T. and their criticisms by others.

In the *Ṛgveda*, references to the Ṛbhus are many[1]. Yāska[2] and

1 *RV.*, I. 20; I. 110; I. 161; I. 164; IX. 33-39 etc. Ṛbhus occur in 11 hymns.

2 Yāska gives the alternative synonyms thus: ऋभव उरू भान्तीति वा। ऋतेन भान्तीति वा। ऋतेन भवन्तीति वा। तेषामेषा भवति ॥ XI. 15 (*The Nighaṇṭu and the Nirukta*, ed. Lakshman Sarup, 1937, p. 194). (1) *Ṛ-bhavaḥ* are (so called because) they shine widely (uru + √bhā), or (2) they shine with sacred rite (ṛta + √bhā), or (3) they live with sacred rite (ṛta + √bhū). (*The Nighaṇṭu and the Nirukta* (Tr.), Lakshman Sarup, 1920, p. 173.)

विष्ट्वी शमी तरणित्वेन वाघतो मर्तासः सन्तो अमृतत्वमानशुः ।
सौधन्वना ऋभवः सूरचक्षसः संवत्सरे समपृच्यन्त धीतिभिः ॥

Rv., I. 110. 4

ऋभुर्विभ्वा वाज इति सुधन्वन आङ्गिरसस्य त्रयः पुत्राः बभूवुः ।
...आदित्यरश्मय ऋभव उच्यन्ते ॥

Nighaṇṭu, XI. 15, 16, p. 194

Having performed laborious works with zeal, institutors of sacrifice, being mortals, they attained immortality. The Ṛbhus, sons of Sudhanvan, radiant like the sun, mixed things together with their works during the year.

Ṛbhu, Vibhvā and Vāja were the three sons of Sudhanvan, a descendant of Āṅgirasa.........

The rays of the sun are called Ṛbhus. Also pp. 172, 173, *Nighaṇṭu* (Tr.)

Sāyaṇa think that the term means the rays of the sun, T. is of opinion that this meaning is not suitable in all cases. For instance, in *Rv.*, I. 161. 13, Ṛbhus should be taken in the sense of seasons, as otherwise the verse becomes meaningless. Accepting this meaning of the term, the story of the Ṛbhus as found in *Rv.*, I. 161 may be stated as follows:

The implication of the term Ṛbhus.

Ṛbhus are 3 in number—Ṛbhu, Vibhvā and Vāja. They represent three seasons[1] in a year recognised in the early Vedic period. Each of these contains roughly 4 months. They are said to re-commence their work at the completion of the year.[2] They do many wonderful things for the gods. Then they take rest for 12 days in the house of Agohya, the 'unconcealable' i. e. the sun. They are thereafter awakened from their sleep. *Vasta* (he-goat) i. e. the sun, gives the information that the hound has awakened them. It is time they should begin their work again. "Then the course begins anew, and anew the earth brings forth fruit, the streams flow; plants cover the heights, and waters, the depths."[3]

The story of Ṛbhus.

19. The story in its simplest form as given above does not look like revealing any facts. T. does not however think that it is as inane as it looks.[4] He tries to explain its inner meaning, and finds one verse in the hymn to be very helpful. The verse runs thus:

Rv., I. 161. 13 reveals the inner meaning of the story.

सुषुप्वांस ऋभवस्तदपृच्छतागोह्य क इदं नो अबूबुधत् ।

श्वानं वस्तो बोधयितारमब्रवीत् संवत्सर इदमद्या व्यख्यत ॥

Rv., I. 161. 13

[Oh Ṛbhus ! you were asleep ; thereafter ask Agohya, who is it that woke us up. The He-goat replied, 'the hound[5] is the awakener'. As the year is passed, today you declare the same.][6]

1 The *Śatapatha Brāhmaṇa* also mentions 3 divisions of the year (XIV 1. 1. 28).

2 *Rv.*, IV. 33. 4

3 *The Orion*, p. 168

4 *Ibid.*, pp, 157-170

5 T. rejects rightly 'wind' as the meaning of श्वानं suggested by Sāyaṇa.

6 W's rendering:

Having slept, ye Ṛbhus, ye asked: 'Who, O agohya, hath awakened us.' The he-goat declares the dog to be the awakener; in a year thus today have ye looked out (i.e., opened your eyes.)—*IA.*, 1895, p. 369

20. As to the proper explanation of the above story, T. states that the three Ṛbhus are three seasons of the year of twelve lunar months. The number of days in such a year is 29½ days × 12 or 354 solar days. But 366 days approximately make one solar year. So, the lunar year is short by 12 days. Ṛbhus were, as it were, genii of the seasons. As the year was a lunar year, "12 days were intercalated at the end of each year to make it correspond with the solar year."[1] The spirits of the seasons stop work for these 12 days and go to sleep. This period belongs neither to the old nor to the new year. It is therefore natural to hold that the hound is some constellation in the heavens, whose appearance indicated the beginning of the year. This hound is none other than the Dog-star or Canis Major. Thus, when the first of the seasons i. e. Vasanta appears, the Dog-star is found in the sky. "In short, the whole story of the Ṛibhus, as we flnd it recorded in the Ṛigveda, directly establishes the fact that at the time when this legend was formed, the year commenced with the vernal equinox in Canis Major or Dog-star."[2] The end of the year is the end of the three seasons here represented by the Ṛbhus.

According to Tilak, 12 days' sleep of Ṛbhus refers to intercalation, and year-beginning at vernal equinox with the Dog-star in the background acc. to the interpretation of the story.

21. W. denies that the hymn has the aforesaid meaning. He finds it unintelligible, and he therefore thinks that any attempt to interpret it is useless. He makes this concession however that he is prepared to admit the truth of T.'s thesis, if 4 conditions mentioned by him are fulfilled. The arguments advanced by him may be summarised as follows:

The 4 conditions laid down by Whitney for admission of the truth of Tilak's theory and how they can be fulfilled.

The Dog (श्वानं in *Rv.*, I. 161. 13) that awakened the Ṛbhus (or, at least, was accused by the 'he-goat', identified with the sun by Yāska, of doing so), in order that they may resume their duties at the beginning of a new year, can be accepted as Canis Major (in Hindu tradition nowhere called Dog), provided the following 4 conditions were fulfilled, viz.

(1) that the Ṛbhus were *divinities* of the season ;

(2) that Agohya, unconcealable one, mentioned in the verse, *was the same as the sun* ;

1 *The Orion*, p. 169

2 *Ibid.*, p, 170

(3) that the *12 days of recreation,* which T. allows to the Ṛbhus, are the 12 days which must be added to make the year a solar one consisting of 366 days ('which neither Vedic tradition nor asronomy sanctions') ;

(4) that 'in a year' ('Saṃvatsare' in the verse) means 'at the end of the year (which might be true if the sleep had been of a year's length, but is far less probable, if not impossible, supposing it to have been of 12 days only').[1]

W. states that the fulfilment of the above conditions would establish "the sun's start upon his yearly round from a vernal equinox in the neighbourhood of Orion, at four to five thousand years before Christ."[2] But as W. is sure that a conclusion depending on so many uncertainties and improbabilities is no conclusion at all, he rejects T.'s conclusion that evidence is found in *Rv.*, I. 161. 13 that in 4000 B.C. or 5000 B C. the year began with the sun at the vernal equinox.

22. Let us see how far these conditions mentioned by W. can be fulfilled.

Condition 1

WHETHER ṚBHUS WERE DIVINITIES

Whitney's *Condition* 1: Evidence of Ṛbhus being divinities.

The *Ṛgveda* states clearly that the Ṛbhus were divinities.

अयं देवाय जन्मने स्तोमो विप्रेभिरासया ।
अकारि रत्नधातमः ॥[3]

Rv., I. 20. 1

[This wealth-giving hymn has been addressed by the sages, by their own mouth, to the (class of) divinities who had been born.[4]]

Keith treats of Ṛbhus as minor gods of nature.[5] He does not deny their divinity.

1 *IA.*, 1895, p. 369

2 *Ibid.*

3 Sāyaṇa explains the verse thus :

ऋभवो हि मनुष्याः सन्तस्तपसा देवत्वं प्राप्ताः । ते चात्र सूक्ते देवताः ।

[Ṛbhus were mortals, *who attained godhood* by austerities. *In this hymn they are the gods praised.*]

For Yāska's explanation, see XI. 15. 16 quoted in para 18, footnote.

4 Based on Wilson, *Rv.* (Tr.), vol. 1, pp. 45, 46

5 A. B. Keith, *Philosophy and Religion of the Veda and Upanishads, I,* (1925), pp. 176-178 : (In the *Ṛgveda*) "they (Ṛbhus) are addressed as gods, and are besought to bestow boons on their worshippers, including the dexterity

Whitney's *Condition 2:* evidence that 'Agohya' refers to the sun,

Condition 2

WHETHER AGOHYA IS THE SUN

23. It is difficult to understand why W. has raised this question at all. For the *Nirukta* XI. 16 clearly says that 'Agohya' is an appellation of Āditya, meaning 'one who cannot be concealed'. It is traced to √ गूह्.

Whitney's *Condition 3:* 12 days' sleep is equivalent to addition of 12 days by way of intercalation.

Condition 3

THE MEANING OF 12 DAYS' SLEEP OF THE ṚBHUS[1]

24. The Ṛgvedic references to year, season, month, days etc. are in several passages not direct, but they are so by implication. For instance,

(a) द्वादशारं नहि तज्जराय वर्वर्ति चक्रं परि द्यामृतस्य ।
आ पुत्रा अग्ने मिथुनासो अत्र सप्त शतानि विंशतिश्च तस्थुः ॥

Rv., I. 164. 11

[The twelve-spoked wheel of the true (sun) revolves round the heavens, and never (tends) to decay: seven hundred and twenty children in pairs, Agni, abide in it.][2]

(b) द्वादश प्रधयश्चक्रमेकं त्रीणि नभ्यानि क उ तच्चिकेत ।
तस्मिन्त्साकं त्रिशता न शङ्कवोऽर्पिताः षष्टिर्न चलाचलासः ॥

Rv., I. 164. 48

[Twelve follies, one wheel, three axles—who knows this? In that wheel are fixed 360 spokes moving and unmoving.][3]

(c) चतुर्भिः साकं नवतिं च नामभिश्चक्रं न वृत्तं व्यतीँरवीविपत् ।

Rv., I. 155. 6

which is theirs specially." But Keith states that "the assertion that the Ṛbhus are really the Ṛtus" is not "in the slightest degree plausible."

[This opinion has been contradicted by what has been stated in para 21.]

1 A. A. Macdonell, *A History of Sanskrit Literature* (1917), p. 106: "They [the Ṛbhus] rested for twelve days in the house of the sun, Agohya ('who cannot be concealed'). This sojourn of the Ṛbhus in the house of the sun in all probability alludes to the winter solstice, the twelve days being the addition which was necessary to bring the lunar year of 354 into harmony with the solar year of nearly 366 days, and was intercalated before the days began to grow perceptibly longer."

2 Wilson, *Rv.* (Tr.), vol. 2, p. 130

3 Cf. Wilson, *Rv.* (Tr.), vol. 2, p. 143

[He causes, by his gyrations, 360 periodical revolutions like a circular wheel.][1]

In the first instance, the reference to months and days of the year is not readily intelligible. 12 spokes stand for 12 months, and 720 children in pairs for 360 days and 360 nights.

In the second example, the references are to 12 months, 1 year, 3 seasons and 360 days.

In the third passage, 1 year is said to have 360 revolutions or days.

In none of the above instances, the word 'days' is to be found after 360. The same remark applies to other references to year, days etc. in the *Ṛgveda*. Hence a question arises as to the sense in which '360' is used. It may mean 360 solar days, or 360 lunar days equivalent to 354 solar days. In either case, it is shorter than the solar year of 366 days, and therefore requires to be intercalated.

Intercalations in the *Ṛgveda*

25. Several passages in the *Ṛgveda* lead us to conclude that Ṛgvedic poets were not unaware of the above-mentioned discrepancies and of the method by which they could be corrected. The correction can be inferred to have been made in any of the following ways:

(1) The addition of 12 days at the end of each year as indicated in *Ṛv*., 163. 13 (see para 19). It was perhaps the earliest method. In that case, '360' means 360 tithis (rotations of the moon) equal to 354 ($29\frac{1}{2} \times 12$) solar days, to which 12 days are added to make the lunar year a solar year. The period during which 12 days were added at the end of each year belonged to an age when only 3 seasons were recognised in a year.

(2) The addition of a full month after $2\frac{1}{2}$ years. This evolved at a later period. The reference to the addition of one month at the end of a year is found in Vedic literature, but nowhere it mentions how many years should elapse before this intercalation was resorted to. The Vedic Indians at one time changed their lunar year into luni-solar one. In that case 1 month was added after $2\frac{1}{2}$ years. But when after a lapse of years Hindus commenced using 'solar year' of 360 days, it fell short of 6 days as compared with full-fledged year. In this case one month was added after 5 years.

1 Sāyaṇa interprets चतुर्भि साकं नवतिं as four and ninety i. e. 94, but the reasonable explanation is four times ninety i.e. 360 as Muir and other scholars point out.

26. The above remarks point to the fact that the number of seasons constituting a year was different at different times. So, T. is right when he states in his *Arctic Home in the Vedas* that as the Aryans entered into India from the North-west, and advanced into the country, the number of seasons experienced by them increased. This explains why the *Ṛgveda* and other Vedic literature mention "three, or five, or six. or even seven seasons (ṛtus) in the year,"[1] against which W. made adverse comments[2] on ancient Hindu Astronomy. From *Rv.*, I.161.13, this much can be known that the method of intercalation adding 12 days to a year must have been the result of observation of the heavens by the ancient Indo-Aryans at a very early stage of their civilization. This hymn was composed in all probability at the dawn of Indo-Aryan civilization, when the number of seasons was three and 12 days were added to a year for changing it into solar one. In other words, intercalation was practised in those early times.

The reason for the mention of different numbers of seasons in the *Ṛgveda*.

27. Two references to the 7th season[3] are given below from the *Ṛgveda*, to show what it really was:

Instances of intercalation by the addition of a month.

(a) साकंजानां सप्तथमाहुरेकजं षळिद्यमा ऋषयो देवता इति ।
तेषामिष्टानि विहितानि धामशः स्थात्रे रेजन्ते विकृतानि रूपशः ॥

Rv., I. 164. 15

[Of those that are born together, sages have called the seventh the single-born ; for six are twins, and are moveable, and born of the gods ; their desirable (properties), placed severally in their proper abodes, are various (also) in form, and revolve for (the benefit of) that which is stationary.][4]

Wilson interprets this verse as follows:

"These are six seasons, made up of two months each ; the seventh is the intercalary month, which has no fellow, and has no *Āditya* to preside over it,[5] wherefore it is not considered to be of

1 Tilak, *Arctic Home in the Vedas*, p. 283

2 *IA.*, 1895, p. 364: "With their customary looseness in regard to such matters, the ancient Hindus reckoned three, or five, or six, or seven seasons (*ritu*) in the year."

3 The 7th season of one month is in reality an 'addition of one month for intercalation after 2½ years or 5 years, as the case may be [see para 24].

4 Wilson, *Rv.* (Tr.), vol. 2, pp. 131, 132

5 Wilson's statement that there is no Āditya to preside over the 7th month is not correct.

divine origin like the rest."[1] "......the several seasons are diversified by the varieties of temperature, produce, and the like, for the benefit of the world."[2]

(b) वेद मासो धृतव्रतो द्वादश प्रजावतः ।

वेदा य उपजायते ॥

Rv., I. 25. 8

[He, who, accepting the rites (dedicated to him), knows the twelve months and their productions, and that which is supplementarily engendered.][3]

Wilson's remarks: "*vedā ya upajāyate*, who knows what is *upa*, additionally, or subordinately, produced. The expression is obscure; but in connexion with the preceding, *veda māso dvādaśa*, who knows the twelve months, we cannot doubt the correctness of the Scholiast's conclusion, that the thirteenth, the supplementary, or intercalary, month of the Hindu luni-solar year is alluded to; 'that thirteenth or additional month which is produced of itself, in connexion with the year',—*yas trayodaśo' dhikamāsa upajāyate saṃvatsarasamīpe svayam evodpadyate.* The passage is important, as indicating the concurrent use of the lunar and solar years at this period, and the method of adjusting the one to the other".[4]

28. The reason for giving some details of intercalation from the *Ṛgveda* is that some scholars do not admit that the ancient Hindus really knew the use of intercalation.

Intercalation was well-known to the Vedic Aryans.

As we shall see later on, Th. does not directly deny that ancient Indians were familiar with the use of intercalation. His attack is based on the supposed ignorance of Indians about the proper length of the year.[5]

29. Keith also speaks in the same strain. He states that the knowledge of the heavenly bodies displayed by the Vedic people

1 Wilson, *Rv.* (Tr.), vol. 2, pp. 131-132 fn.

2 *Ibid.*, p. 132 fn.

3 *Ibid.*, vol. I, p. 65

4 *Ibid.*, pp. 65-66 fn.

5 *IA.*, 1895, p. 99: "What here immediately concerns us is the recognition of the fact that anything, like a fairly accurate fixation of the sun's place among the stars at the winter solstice, cannot be imagined to have been accomplished by people who had no approximately correct notion of the length of the year."

Keith's criticism is based on his wrong interpretation of passages, and confusion regarding intercalation.

is the most meagre possible, that planets were unknown to the *Ṛgveda*, that there is no proof of worship of any heavenly bodies other than the sun and the moon in the *Ṛgveda*, and that the rudimentary knowledge of even the division of time is seen in the fact that a year of 360 days and 12 months is, apart from the occasional mention of a 10-month year of gestation, the only year clearly known to the whole of Vedic literature prior to the later Sūtras.

It is to be regretted that Keith nowhere tries to grasp the full meaning of a year of 360 days. He has, however, to admit that the ancient Indians had knowledge of intercalation. Thus says he: "That the year of 12 months, which seems to have been a rough adaptation to the solar year of the synodic month of between 29 and 30 days, was not a perfect year seems, however, to have been recognised, for the Rigveda already contains the mention of a thirteenth supplementary month which must, we may assume, have been intercalated periodically, but there is no evidence worth serious consideration for the view that the Vedic period knew a period of five years as a unit for intercalation."[1]

Though Keith admits that ancient Indians had knowledge of intercalation, he confuses the issue when he states that no mention of intercalation after 5 years is made in the Vedic literature. In fact, as has already been pointed out, it is only by reference to particular passages that we can understand whether intercalation is made after one year or 2½ years or 5 years. So, it is in vain that Keith seeks to conclude that the unit for each intercalation was five years, without taking due note of other passages in the *Ṛgveda*. That point is discussed by Macdonell and Keith also in *Vedic Index*[2] while treating of Vedic year and month. They state

How Macdonell and Keith misinterpret Ṛbhus.

that numerous passages in the *Ṛgveda* speak of 12 months or 360 days for a year, but they contend against the fact that the Vedic period was acquainted with the year of 354 days. They also reject Zimmer's assertion that in *Rv.*, I. 161. 13 an attempt has been made at intercalation. Macdonell and Keith hold that as the *Ṛgveda* does not directly refer to intercalation anywhere, the 12 days "are merely the 'reflexion of the year' (*saṃvatsarasya pratimā*) in the same way

1 Keith, *The Religion and Philosophy of the Veda and Upaniṣads*, 1, p. 79

2 A. A. Macdonell and A. B. Keith, *Vedic Index of Names and Subjects* (1912), vol. 2, *S.V. Saṃvatsara*, pp. 411-413 ; *S.V. Māsa*, pp. 156-163

that they represent the twelve months and have no relation to chronology at all".

It is easy to see that the authors do not take note of the main issue. Scholars of their eminence need not be told that non-mention of intercalation in the *Ṛgveda* does not prove its non-existence as has been shown in para 19.

Whitney on the year being 366 days long.

30. W. on the other hand contends that neither Vedic tradition nor Vedic astronomy sanctions a year of 366 days, and therefore the idea of intercalation is uncalled for. W. would have been correct if the 7th season or the 13th month (presumably for intercalation) had not been mentioned.[1] The Vedic Indians, as their astronomical knowledge advanced, added 12 days after a year, or one month after $2\frac{1}{2}$ lunar, or 5 solar, years, of 360 days.

By intercalation the ancient Hindus corrected not only the error in each year, but also the error that remained after first intercalation.

31. As the ancient Indo-Aryans converted the lunar year into a solar one by adding 12 days after a year of 354 days or one month (30 days) after two years and a half, the 366 days in the year contained an error of 3/4 day in each year. Even at the time of the *Ṛgveda,* this did not escape the observation of the Indo-Aryans. They discovered a way to correct this small error. It is briefly stated below.

The six seasons have six presiding deities (Ādityas). The 7th Āditya presides over the 7th season of one month[1]. The number of Ādityas presiding over seasons is said to be 8. Hence, the 8th Āditya must have some season over which to preside. The 8th Āditya is the presiding deity of one month that has to be thrown away after each 40 years. The fact is that if we admit that in each year of 366 days an error of 3/4th of a day creeps in, we have also to admit that after 40 years the error becomes as big as one month (because $40x3/4=30$ days). One month's error after 40 years is not a negligible thing ; and this error could not be allowed to continue indefinitely, for that would have vitiated astronomical calculations, and religious performances. The Indo-Aryans corrected it by deducting one month from a year after every 40 years. It cannot be concieved that those who were so eager to intercalate the year by adding 12 days or 1 month, as the case may be, would not care to correct this mistake of a month each 40

1 See para 27.

years. Evidence of this correction is found in the following verses of the *Ṛv.*[1]

अष्टौ पुत्रासो अदितेर्ये जातास्तन्वस्परि ।

देवाँ उप प्रैत् सप्तभिः परा मार्ताण्डमास्य ॥८॥

सप्तभिः पुत्रैरदितिरुप प्रैत् पूर्व्यं युगं ।

प्रजायै मृत्यवे त्वत् पुनर्मार्ताण्डमाभरत् ॥९

[Eight sons (there were) of Aditi who were born from her body; she approached the gods with seven, but threw away Mārtāṇḍa. 8

In a former yuga, Aditi went with seven sons, but she bore Mārtāṇḍa again for the sake of death. 9]

Ādityas are the sons of Aditi. Seven of them stand for seven seasons. But the reference to the 8th Āditya called Mārtāṇḍa (mārta + aṇḍa = dead egg) has a special significance. For, while Aditi presents the first seven sons to the gods, she throws away i.e. bears him (the eighth) for the sake of death. This Āditya, though a deity like the other Ādityas, is not of their category. Description about him becomes meaningful only when we connect this deity (as a presiding deity) with a season (of one month) which is thrown away or given to death and not added (to a year). This is the only way in which परा मार्त्ताण्डमास्यात् or प्रजायै मृत्यवे.. मार्ताण्डमभरत् can be explained. As we have seen, the necessity for adding 12 days to each year for converting it into a solar one was felt from very early times. This contained an error which needed correction.

It is stated that Indra discovered Śambara concealed in the mountains after a search of 40 years.

यः शंवरं पर्वतेषु क्षियन्तं चत्वारिंश्यां शरद्यन्वविंदत् ।

ओजायमान यो अहिं जघान दानुं शयानं स जनास इन्द्रः ॥[2]

[He, who discovered Śambara dwelling in the mountains for forty years ; who slew Ahi, growing in strength, and the sleeping son of Danu ; he, men, is Indra].[3]

In other words, the above verses indicate the journey of Indra (the sun) for 40 years. In 40 solar years, each of 366 days, the excess amounts to $\frac{3}{4}$ (of a day each year) $\times 40 = 30$ days. This month of 30 days should be deducted after every 40 years to make the length of the year equal to 365 $\frac{1}{4}$ days.

1 *Rv.*, X. 72. 8-9
2 *Ibid.*, II.12,11
3 Wilson, *Rv.* (T.), vol. 2, pp. 237, 238

The conclusion becomes irresistible that the method of correcting the small error of 3/4 of a day every year after 40 years was known to the ancient Hindus.[1]

Condition 4

WHETHER SAṂVATSARE MEANS 'IN A YEAR'

Whitney's *Condition 4*: Meaning of 'Saṃvatsare'.

32. W. feels diffident about the sense in which the word Saṃvatsare has been used in *Rv.*, 1. 161. 13.[2] It is not clear however what other rendering would have been better than 'in a year.' If what he intends to state be that 12 days' sleep did not take place at the end of the year, but at any time during the year, it makes no difference, because even in that case there is an addition of 12 days. But if we turn our attention to the text, we find that the end of the year is indicated. Otherwise the last portion of the verse viz. इदमद्या व्यख्यत (you declare this today), that it is the end of the year, becomes irrelevant.

Tilak fulfils the 4 conditions laid down by Whitney.

33. From the foregoing observations, one can easily see that the 4 conditions set by W. have been fulfilled by T. One has therefore to conclude that T.'s interpretation of *Rv.*, I. 161. 13 is the only one that can be accepted, and that the sun commenced its course for a new year from the vernal equinox in Mṛgaśiras (of which the Dog-star is a part), after the lapse of 12 days that were intercalated.

In Hindu tradition Canis Major was called श्वान (Dog-star): Whitney's denial is challenged by Tilak.

34. Before leaving this subject, a point raised by W. requires consideration. W. denies that the star Canis Major was called श्वान (Dog-star) anywhere in Hindu tradition. T. gives several instances to prove that Canis Major was called श्वान (Dog). These must have escaped W.'s notice, as otherwise he would not have made the remarks mentioned above.

1 Vide Jogesh Ch. Rāy, *Veder Devatā O Kṛṣṭikāla* (Vedic gods and age of Vedic culture), 1954, pp. 88ff.

2 See para 19.

सुषुप्वांस ऋभवस्तदपृच्छतागोह्य क इदं नो अबूबुधत् ।
श्वानं वस्तो बोधयितारमब्रवीत् संवत्सर इदमद्या व्यख्यत ॥

[Oh Ṛbhus! You were asleep; thereafter ask Agohya who is that woke us up. The He-goat replied, 'the hound is the awakener'. As the year is passed , today you declare the same.]

Some of the instances are reproduced below :

(a) अति द्रव सारमेयौ श्वानौ चतुरक्षौ शबलौ साधुना पथा ।
अथा पितॄन्त्सुविदत्राँ उपेहि यमेन ये सधमादं मदन्ति ॥१०
यौ ते श्वानौ यम रक्षितारौ चतुरक्षौ पथिरक्षी नृचक्षसौ ।
ताभ्यामेनं परि देहि राजन्त् स्वस्ति चास्मा अनमीवं च धेहि ॥११
उरूणसावसुतृपा उदुम्बलौ यमस्य दूतौ चरतो जनाँ अनु ।
तावस्मभ्यं दृशये सूर्याय पुनर्दातामसुमद्येह भद्रम् ॥१२[1]

[(The description of two dogs near the gates of Yama.) Pass by a secure path beyond the two spotted four-eyed Dogs, the progeny of Saramā, and join the wise *pitṛs* who rejoice joyfully with Yama. 10

Entrust him, O King, to thy two Dogs, which are thy protectors, Yama, the four-eyed guardians of the road, renowned by men, and grant him prosperity and health. 11

The messengers of Yama, broad-nosed, and of exceeding strength, and satiating themselves with the life (of mortals), hunt mankind; may they allow us this day a prosperous existence here, that we may look upon the sun. 12][2]

Read with *Ṛv.*, X. 10 (the dialogue between Yama and Yamī), the above passage indicates that two sons (dogs) of Saramā (the bitch of heaven) guarded the gates of heaven (the Milky Way). They can be easily identified with Canis Major and Canis Minor on both sides of the Milky Way. The mention of milk suggests that it must be the milk in the galaxy with two dogs on each side.[3]

(b) *Rv.*, X, 108 is a dialogue between Saramā and the Paṇis. The latter had taken away the cows of Indra, who sent his messenger Saramā in search of them. After travelling in most distant places she met the Paṇis. They tried to coax her to remain with them and enjoy their wealth, but failed. On her return, she denied having seen the cows cf Indra, at which Indra kicked her, and she vomitted milk. This looks like the Milky Way with which Saramā's connectton is established.[4]

T. points out that Śunāśirau in *Ṛv.*, IV. 57. 5 is considered by

1 *Rv.*, X. 14
2 Wilson, *Rv.*, (Tr.), vol. 6, p. 33
3 Tilak, *The Orion*, pp. 112, 113
4 *Ibid.*, p. 113

M. to be a very old name of the Dog-star[1] (in dual). The 5th *ṛk* in IV. 57 runs as follows:

शुनासीराविमां वाचं जुषेथां यद्दिवि चक्रथुः पयः ।
तेनेमामुपसिञ्चतम् ॥

Rv., IV. 57. 5

[Śuna and Sīra be pleased by this our praise, and consequently sprinkle this (earth) with the water which you have created in heaven][2] According to T. Śunāśīrau are invoked in order that they may pour down upon the earth the "milk" which they "make in heaven".[3]

Thus the assertion of W. that Canis Major was nowhere called श्वान (Dog-star) in Hindu tradition cannot stand.

(2) VṚṢĀKAPI

The gist of the story contained in the Vṛṣākapi hymn,—*Ṛv.*, x.86.

35. The Vṛṣākapi hymn (*Ṛv.*, X. 86), remarkable in many ways, may be cited as an evidence of the antiquity of the *Ṛgveda*. Different scholars have interpreted it differently and reached diverse conclusions.[4] But the explanation of this hymn as given by T. seems to me cogent for reasons that will be presently stated.

The hymn is elaborately treated by T. Mainly following him, the gist of the story contained in it is as follows:

It was a common practice with the Vedic people to offer sacrifices to Indra for adequate rains and good crops. By the sacrifices, the prayers of the sacrificers are granted. Rains come and abundant crops appear. [Towards the end of rainy season] the sacrifices to Indra are stopped, and people who bring sacrificial things for Indra leave the same at his temple without offering them to him and are therefore wasted. They offer new sacrifices to Vṛṣākapi. Indrāṇī takes this as an affront to her Lord and becomes very angry with Vṛṣākapi, who, she thinks, is responsible for all this mischief. She makes up her mind to punish him. She says that she will not be satisfied till she can set the Dog, eager for a

1 Cf. Max Müller. *Lectures on the Science of Language*, vol. 2, p. 526
2 Wilson, *Rv.* (Tr.), vol. 3, pp. 224, 225
3 Tilak, *The Orion*, p. 113
4 'This is a somewhat unintelligible *Sūkta*'—Wilson (Tr.), vol. 6, p. 236 fn.

chase of hog, on Vṛṣākapi (हरितो मृगः, the yellow antelope) to bite him in the ear,[1] or behead the evil-doer.[2]

Indra however finds no cause for anger with Vṛṣākapi. He is rather glad that his friend (सखा) Vṛṣākapi has appeared in time to do his duty viz. giving wealth in the shape of good crops to the people, who in turn are offering sacrifices to Vṛṣākapi in lieu of Indra. But Indrāṇī has to be pacified. So Indra begins to praise the beauty of her person and her many qualities,[3] and requests her to forgive Vṛṣākapi.[4]

Indrāṇī does not relent. Failing to rouse up Indra's ire against Vṛṣākapi, Indrāṇi now relates to Indra the great anguish and humiliation to which she has been subjected by Vṛṣākapi for diverting the people to make sacrifices to himself instead of to her husband and thereby rendering useless the sources of pleasure to her. This attempt of Indrāṇī also fails. For, Indra cannot forsake his friend.[5]

How long can a woman (be she a goddess) resist the persuasions of a husband like Indra? Indrāṇī relents at last and orders the wife of Vṛṣākapi to invite Indra to a feast where bulls may be served to him.[6] This satisfies Indra who informs Indrāṇī that arrangement for his feast has been made.[6]

1 श्वा न्वस्य जंभिषदपि कर्णे वराहयु : etc. ॥४॥

[(Indrānī to Indra) Let the dog, eager (to chase) a hog *(varāha)*, bite him at his ear.] —*The Orion*, p. 181

2 प्रिया तष्टानि मे कपिर्व्यक्ता व्यदूदुषत् ।

शिरो न्वस्य राविषं न सुगं दुष्कृते भुवम् etc. ॥५॥

[The kapi spoilt my favourite things. I shall, therefore, cut off his head, in order that an evil-doer may not enjoy happiness.]—*The Orion*, pp. 181, 182

3 Verses 7, 8, 10, 11

4 Verse 12

5 वृषाकपायि रेवति सुपुत्र आदु सुस्नुषे ।

घसत्त इंद्र उक्षणः प्रियं काचित्करं हविः etc. ॥१३॥

[O rich Vṛṣākapāyī! having a good son and a daughter-in-law, let Indra swallow the bulls, your favourite and delightful oblation.]—*The Orion*, p. 184. Presumably this is addressed by Indrānī to Vṛṣākapāyī, wife of Vṛṣākapī.

6 उक्षणो हि मे पंचदश साकं पचन्ति विंशतिम् ।

उताहमद्मि पीव इदुभा कुक्षी प्रीणंति मे etc. ॥१४॥

[Twenty and fifteen oxen are being cooked for me; I shall eat them and be fat. Both the sides of my belly will be filled up.]—*The Orion*, p. 185

Then, at Indrāṇī's desire, Indra sports with her, as a bull sports among the cows. Indrāṇī is gratified and forgives Vṛṣākapi.[1]

Thus a reconciliation takes place. Indrāṇī's heart softens so much that she invites Vṛṣākapi, through Indra, to cook and partake of the meat of a slain animal (an antelope), and she supplies materials for cooking the same[2]. [This antelope has nothing to do with the yellow antelope with which Vṛṣākapi has been identified in verse 3]. This turn of events pleases Indra.[3]

Then comes the time for Vṛṣākapi to descend to hiṣ nether house. As friendship has grown, he is invited either by Indra or by Indrāṇī to come again to their house.[4]

Vṛṣākapi is addressed as the disturber of sleep. It is said that sacrifice will commence when he appears again.[5]

In this way the cycle goes on and on. Whenever Vṛṣākapi appears, the great offender Mṛga, who misleads people, can be seen no more. There is no knowing where he has gone.[6]

1 Verses 15, 16 and 17

2 अयमिंद्र वृषाकपिः परस्वन्तं हतं विदत् ।

असिं सूनां नवं चरुमादेधस्यान आचितम् etc. ॥ १८ ॥

[O Indra! let Vṛṣākapi get the slain animal. Let him at once have a knife, a fire-place, a new vessel, and a cartload of firewood (to cook the killed animal)]—*The Orion*, pp. 185, 186

3 अयमेमि विचाकशद्विचिन्वन्दासमार्यम् ।

पिबामि पाकसुत्वनोऽभि धीरमचाकशं etc. ॥ १९ ॥

[Thus do I go seeing and discriminating between a *dāsa* and an *ārya* I take my drink from those that prepare Soma juice and cook the oblation thus and behold (or protect) the intelligent sacrificers.]—*The Orion*, p. 186

4 धन्व च यत् कृन्तत्रं च कतिस्वित्ता वि योजना ।

नेदीयसो वृषाकपेऽस्तमेहि गृहाँ उप etc. ॥ २० ॥

[O Vṛṣākapi ! go to the house—the celestial sphere which is cut off and which contains some (unknown) *yojanas* or stages. From your *nether* house come to our house.]—*The Orion*, p. 191

5 पुनरेहि वृषाकपे सुविता कल्पयावहै ।

य एषः स्वप्नंशनोऽस्तमेषि पथा पुनः etc. ॥ २१ ॥

[O Vṛṣākapi ! you, the destroyer of sleep, who are going to the house, come back again, again by (your) way. We would perform the sacrifices.]—*The Orion*, p. 192

6 यदुदंचो वृषाकपे गृहमिंद्राजगन्तन ।

क्वस्य पुल्वघो मृगः कमगञ्जनयोपनो etc. ॥ २२ ॥

[O mighty Vṛṣākapi ! when you rising upwards (or rather northwards) would come to (our) house, where would that great sinner Mṛga be? Where he, who misleads people, would go?]—*The Orion*, pp. 193, 194

Vṛṣākapi means the sun at the autumnal equinox, according to Tilak.

36. It is easy to follow the thread of the story from the above gist.[1] The main question requiring solution in regard to this hymn is the identity of Vṛṣākapi.

T. after giving a translation of the whole hymn verse by verse with detailed explanations,[2] points out that the word Vṛṣākapi has usually been taken by scholars in the sense of the sun in one or other form, and that in the present hymn it is used to convey a special meaning viz. the sun at the autumnal equinox, with the Dog-star (a part of Mṛgaśiras) in the background, and the equinoctial year begins. The sun at that time can rightly be spoken of as to have shaken off the rains, for just after the rains an equinox is reached.

37. W. ridicules T.'s interpretation of Vṛṣākapi and dismisses it with the following words:

Whitney rejects Tilak's theory without assigning any reason.

"The use made of it (i.e. the Vṛṣākapi hymn) seems utterly fanciful and unwarranted. Of all who have attempted to bring sense out of that strange and obscure passage of the *Ṛig-veda,* no one is less to be congratulated on his success than Mr. Tilak. His discussion of it is only to be paralleled with the endeavour to extract sunbeams from cucumbers, and does not in the least call for examination or criticism in detail."[3]

W. has rejected the whole theory of T., but it is regrettable that a scholar of W.'s eminence should advance no agruments to disprove T.'s contention.[4] Had he done so, counter-arguments could have been produced.

1 The 23rd or last verse of the hymn runs thus:

पर्शुर्ह नाम मानवी साकं ससूव विंशतिम् ।

भद्रं भल त्यस्या अभूद्यस्या उदरमामयद्विश्व etc. ॥

It does not appear to have any bearing on the story proper. It is a mere statement that Parśus, daughter of Manu, bore 20 sons. Some intervening verses might have been lost, for which a connection cannot be established with previous verses.

2 *The Orion*, pp. 170-197. It is not easy to guess rightly the speakers of different verses. M. in his letter to Burnell, dated Jan. 26, 1874 says: "In the hymn X. 86 there is considerable uncertainty as to the persons to whom each verse is to be assigned."—Max Müller, *Rv.*, (Text), vol. VI, intr., p. XXV

3 *I.A.*, 1895, p. 369

4 Cf. *The Life and Letters of the Rt. Hon'ble Friedrich Max Müller* (in 2 vols), ed by his wife, Longmans, Green & Co. 1902, vol. 2, p. 31

Keith takes Vṛṣākapi to be a male-ape, over whom Indra and Indrāṇī's quarrel is depicted inthe hymn.

38. Keith also discusses the hymn. He renders the word Vṛṣākapi as male-ape. His comment on the hymn is given below: "One of the most obscure hymns of the Rigveda tells us of a dispute between Indra and Indrāṇī over a being styled Vṛṣākapi, 'male-ape'; to seek in it a naturalistic interpretation is rendered from the outset almost hopeless when we recognize that the chief figure in the dispute, the angry Indrāṇī, is clearly not a nature personification in any sense."[1]

In another context, Keith discusses the Frog Song, *Rv*. VIII. 103 and does not think it proper to take it as a satirical one. In his opinion, such a hymn would not have been preserved, if it had no religious or magic basis. "The Vṛṣākapi hymn which shows Indra and Indrāṇī in dispute over a male ape may be adduced in this connexion, but in the absence of any surety as to its meaning it is difficult to rely upon it."[2]

Keith does not find anything more in this hymn than a dispute between Indra and Indrāṇī (a god and a goddess) for a male-ape. It is not reasonble to think that the Vedic poets would give a permanent place to a small and frivolous matter in their sacred treatise, the *Ṛgveda*, unless something more serious and significant had been meant.

Keith's remarks on this hymn are not, in short, helpful in arriving at that meaning.

Identity of Vṛṣākapi.

39. A hint as to the indentity of Vṛṣākapi is to be found in the reference to Vṛṣākapi as the disturber of sleep (स्वप्नंशन:)[3] and to the Mṛga who is said to have disappeared on the appearance of Vṛṣākapi क्वस्य पुल्वघो मृग: (where is the offensive Mṛga gone?). Verse 21 refers to the rising of an object (Vṛṣākapi) to awaken the world, and verse 22 to the disappearance of Mṛga (a star) on the appearance of the object in the sky.

Yāska and Sāyaṇa have not been able to get at the real meaning.

40. T. states that both Sāyaṇa and Yāska have not been able to get at the real meaning of Mṛga, which is Mṛgaśiras according to him.[4]

1 A. B. Keith, *Philosophy and Religion of the Veda and Upanishads*, I, p. 61

2 *Ibid*., 2, p. 434

3 Verse 22

4 Tilak, *The Orion*, pp. 193, 194

Yāska explains *Rv*. X. 86. 21.

41. Yāska, an ancient commentator of some of the verses of the *Ṛgveda*, picks up in his *Nirukta*, verse 21. Lakshman Sarup renders it into English thus: [Indra speaks to Vṛṣākapi:] "O Vṛṣākapi, thou who art the destroyer of dreams, who are about to set along the path once more ; come again. We two will regulate the prosperous course."[1]

Yāska explains the word Vṛṣākapi thus: अथ यं रश्मिभिरभिप्रकम्पयेन्नेति तद् वृषाकपि र्भवति । वृषाकम्पनः । 12. 27.[2] (Now he, who with his rays, causes everything to quiver, is called Vṛṣākapi, i.e. the shaker with rays.)[3]

Yāska's explanation of the verse is translated as follows:

"O Vṛṣākpi, thou art the destroyer of dreams,—i.e. the sun, by rising (in the morning), causes dreams to be destroyed. As such thou art about to set along the path once more. Come again, we two will regulate the well-stimulated actions".[4]

Vṛṣākapi is terrifier of rains.

42. Vṛṣākapi should, I think, be taken as 'terrifier of rains' (vṛṣā=rains, kapi=one who terrifies. If the hymn be carefully analysed, it will be found that it speaks of the arrival of autumn which compels the disappearance of rains through fright. Abundance of crops is noticed, rains falling into disfavour.

Rv, X. 86, points to a time when Mṛgaśras or Dog-star appeared in the sky, the sun being at the autumnal equinox.[5]

1 Verse 21 is cited by Yāska to show the use of the word Vṛṣākapi, the shaker with its rays. See Lakshman Sarup's ed. *Nighaṇṭu and Nirukta*, Text, p. 215 and Tr., p. 192

2 Sarup, *Nighaṇṭu and Nirukta*, Text, p. 215

3 *Ibid*., Tr., 193

वर्षतीति वृषा [मेघः] इन्द्रो (वा)
कम्पते अकम्पते अस्मात् इति ।

Bhāniyi Dikshit on Amara

[That which showers rain is Vṛṣā (cloud) or Indra. From it comes the shaking,]

4 पुनरेहि वृषाकपे सुप्रसूतानि वः कर्माणि
कल्पयावहै । य एष । स्वप्ननंशनः । स्वप्नान्नाशयति ।

Sarup, Text, p. 215

5 In passing, I should mention that it has been suggested that *Rv*., X. 86 is nothing but the story of displacement of Indra-worship by Vṛṣākapi (Sun), worship. But nothing like permanent displacement is hinted at anywhere in the hymn. If that were the purpose, then every śloka in the hymn would not have ended by extolling Indra (विश्वस्मादिन्द्रः उत्तर :). This repetition of

(3) THE MAṆḌUKAS
(Frogs)

The views of different scholars on the Frog-song, *Rv.* VII. 103.

43. A complete hymn of the *Ṛgveda* viz. VII. 103 is devoted to the description and praise of the Frogs. These creatures are neither symbols of gods nor subjects of respect from the people. There must therefore have been special reasons for which this hymn found a permanent place in the sacred book, the *Ṛgveda*.

Max Müller.

Interpreted in the above light, M.'s remarks that the hymn is a satire on the priests, the elaborate ceremonial of the Brāhmaṇs being actually turned into ridicule, are beside the mark. M. states that it was curious to observe that the said animals "should have been chosen by the Vedic satirist to represent the priests, which by the earliest satirist of Greece was selected as the representatives of the Homeric heroes."[1]

Whitney.

W. finds the hymn to be simply a humorous one.[2]

Macdonell and Keith.

Macdonell and Keith do not subscribe to the above view of M.: "It has been explained by Max Müller as a satire on the Brāhmins. Geldner, agreeing with this view, thinks that it is directed by Vasiṣṭha composer against rival Brāhmins, probably the Viśvāmitras. The view, however, which interprets the hymn as a rain charm seems on the whole more likely."[3]

Macdonell.

Macdonell in his *History of Sanskrit Literature* calls it a late hymn. According to him, though the hymn is entirely secular in style, its original purpose is doubtful. He thinks that "the awakening of the frogs at the beginning of the rainy season is here described with a graphic power which will doubtless be appreciated best by those who have lived in India. The poet compares the din of this croaking with the chants of the priests exhilarated by Soma, and with the clamour of pupils at school repeating the words of their teacher."[4] Macdonell further

Indra's superiority would not have been made, if Vṛṣākapi-worship had permanently displaced Indra-worship. The real intention underlying the hymn is to point out that at the advent of autumn, Vṛṣākapi-worship was more important because it ushered in wealth and prosperity in the shape of crops.

1 Max Müller, *History*, p. 255

2 *IA.*, 1895, p. 362

3 Macdonell and Keith, *Vedic Index* (1912), vol. 2, pp. 120, 121

4 Macdonell, *History of Sanskrit literature*, p. 121

states that if the purpose of the hymn be satire upon priests, then how can it have gained admittance into a collection like the *Ṛgveda*, edited if not composed, by priests? It is not possible that Brāhmins were ignorant of the signification of the poem.[1]

Keith.

Keith does not deny an element of humour in the hymn, but he is not prepared to take it as a mere satire on the Brāhmins, for such a hymn would not then have been preserved.[2]

Read with the previous hymns the meaning of the Frog-song becomes clearer.

The above instances show that the interpretations of the Frog-song by different scholars are diverse. The hymn is not difficult to understand, if it is looked at in its proper perspective. It should not be detached from the two previous hymns. These three hymns (101-103) of the 7th Maṇḍala of the *Ṛgveda* are all prayers to the god of clouds (Parjanya) for shower of rain. Anybody desirous of having rains should immerse himself in water up to the mouth and recite repeatedly the first two hymns. His desire will then be fulfilled, Sāyaṇa following Śaunaka in the Ṛgvidhāna states that if prayer is made in the aforesaid manner, rain would surely fall on the 5th night.

The *Nirukta*[3] points out that the 3rd hymn is an invocation by sage Vasiṣṭha to god Parjanya for rainfall. As the frogs supported him by croaking, they were praised by Vasiṣṭha.

This is the background which helps the interpretation of this particular hymn.

Importance of the 9th verse of *Rv*. VII. 103.

44. Some scholars think that hymn 103 of *Rv*. VII is of great importance as they find in the verse indication of the time when it was composed. Others again emphasise that the attempt to prove the antiquity of the *Ṛgveda* from the verse is futile. This led to a controversy in regard to the right interpretation of the verse, or rather of one word of the verse,[4] *dvādaśasya*.

1 *Ibid.*, 121

2 Keith, *The Religion and Philosophy of Veda and Upaniṣads*, I, p. 141, and 2, p. 434

3 *Nirukta*, 9. 6

4 The degree of importance attached to the Frog-song (VII. 103) may be realised from the fact that it has drawn attention of many scholars and has been dealt with by Max Müller, in his *History*, p. 258 ; Macdonell, in his *History of Sanskrit Literature*, 1919, pp. 121, 122 ; Wilson, in his *Rigveda* (Tr.), vol. IV, p. 202; Kaegi and Geldner, in their *Rigveda*, (Tr.); Jacobi in *I.A.*, 1894, pp. 154ff; Macdonell and Keith, in their *Vedic Index*, vol. 2,

The ṛk in question runs thus:

देवहितिं जुगुपुर्द्वादशस्य ऋतुं नरो न प्र मिनन्त्येते ।
संवत्सरे प्रावृष्यागतायां तप्ता घर्मा अश्नुवते विसर्गम् ॥

VII. 103. 9

It has been translated in the following two ways:

(1) 'They observe the sacred order, never forget the proper time of the *twelfth* (*month*), these men. As soon as in the year the raintime has come, the hot glow of the sun finds its end' (Jacobi).

(2) 'They observe the sacred order of *the year*, they never forget the proper time, those men, as soon as in the year the raintime has come, the hot glow of the sun finds its end' (Keigi and Geldner).

The meaning of dvādaśasya in the verse.

45. In translating the ṛk, the question arises, in what sense the word *dvādaśasya* should be taken. It may mean twelfth or twelve-fold, and the significance of the whole verse changes accordingly.

Jacobi's interpretation of the term dvādaśasya as twelfth instead of twelve.

46. J.'s preference is for 'twelfth'. He reproduces the rendering of Kaegi and Geldner, which is as follows: "Sie halten ain des Jahres heilige Ordnung Vergs sen nie die rechte zeita, die Männer, sobald im Jahr die Regenzeit gekomnen die heirse sonnemglut ein Ende findet".[1] Grassman also translates it in a similar way.

J. on the whole accepts Kaegi and Geldner's rendering, but objects 'to the translation of dvādaśa into year' (12 months).[2] He does not deny the possibility of this meaning, for it can also mean 'with twelve parts'. "Dvādaśa strotra in the *Śatapatha Brāhmaṇa* and *Taittirīya Brāhmaṇa* has this meaning". In his opinion, however, this meaning should not be attached to the word when it stands alone i.e. when the thing which has twelve parts is not mentioned. Therefore, in this passage he takes the word *dvādaśasya*, 'with māsaḥ understood'. Hence, J. translates the first portion in the following way: "They observe the sacred order,

pp. 120, 121; Keith, in his *Religion and Philosophy of the Veda*, I, p. 141, and 2, p. 434.

1 "They observe the sacred order of the year, they never forget the proper time, those men, as soon as in the year the raintime has come the hot glow of the sun finds its end."

2 Sāyaṇa makes *dvādaśasya ṛtum* equivalent to *dvādaśa-masātmākasya samvatsarasya ṛtum tam Vasantādikam* i.e. the season beginning with Vasanta (spring) of the year 'with twelve'. —Max Müller, *History*, p. 269

never forget the proper time of the twelfth (month), these men." From this he concludes that he has for the *Ṛgveda* "a year beginning with rainy season, the most obvious and in general most regular division of time, from which the later Hindus called the year *Varshā* or *abda* (=ap+da, rain-giving)". The first rain comes about the summer solstice. So this passage in the *Rv.* may be a reference to rainy season and summer solstice. J. states that "Those sensible creatures (naraḥ)—the frogs are therefore justly praised for never forgetting the right month, the twelfth (month) and with it the proper divisions of the seasons."[1]

Whitney.

W. thinks that J.'s finding from the particular verse that, the beginning of the year was determined by the beginning of the rainy season, cannot be supported. According to him, "*Dvādaśa* does not in fact mean twelfth any more naturally than twelve-fold ; its ordinal value, though commoner, especially in later time, is not one whit more original and proper than the other, or than yet others ; and the proposed change partly as agreeing less with the metrical division of the verse, is, in my opinion, no improvement, but rather the contrary ; and no conclusion as to the beginning of the year can be drawn from it with any fair degree of confidence."[2]

Thibaut.

Th. finds J.'s arguments regarding mention of year-beginning in the *Rv.* unconvincing. He states that J.'s attempt to show that there are traces in the *Rv.* of a beginning of the year in the rains, is futile, because "there is in fact, no reason why any of the three great seasons[3] should not, from certain points of view, have been looked upon as the first, and the beginning of the rains is certainly the most striking of the seasonal phenomena of the Indian year." Though he does not object to the idea that the year was later called *varṣā* or *abda*, he cannot support the interpretation of the verse 103. 9 of the 7th Maṇḍala that the twelfth month of the year occurs about the time of the beginning of the rains. In this, he is at one with A. Weber, *Vedischa Beiträge*, 1894, p. 34 and E. Windish, Z. D. M. G., vol. 48, p. 356 ; "for *dvādaśasya* in that verse certainly means the year (*saṃvatsara*)—mentioned immediately afterwards—which consists of twelve months."[4]

1 *IA.*, 1894, p. 154
2 *IA.*, 1895, p. 362
3 Hīmā, Varṣā, Śarad
4 *IA.*, 1895, p. 95

Not wholly supported by Bühler.

B. points out first that J. and T. have been able to establish that the Vedic Phālguna, Prauṣṭhapada, and Mārgaśīrṣa years began respectively with the winter and summer solstices and the autumnal equinox.[1]

B. then considers two other additional points of J. He states that according to J.'s interpretation, देवहितिं जुगुपुर्द्वादशस्य ऋतुं नरो न प्रमिनन्त्यते, means "they guard the sacred order, these males never forget the proper time of the twelfth (month)". "The passage thus alleges that the frogs are annually resuscitated in the twelfth month, of course the last of the hot season, and it indicates that the year began with the rains or about the summer solstice."[2] In spite of his own experience however he advises caution. As the all-important word dvādaśa is ambiguous, and may mean also 'the (year) consisting of twelve (parts)', he is reluctant to put any great value on a line which may be translated, "they keep the sacred order of the year, these males never forget the proper season—whereby the allusion to the Varṣā is lost." B. therefore rejects J'.s rendering of the verse.[3]

But when properly construed, it means 'twelfth' in its context.

47. It is true that in the interpretation of the above-mentioned verse, different scholars have translated it in different ways, but it will be found that the western scholars are generally in favour of taking dvādaśasya in the sense of twelve month rather than twelfth (month). Even J. who treated it first in the sense of twelfth, had to authorise B. to state that J. was fully aware of the objection which may be raised against his argument, and that it was not to be considered of first importance.[4]

This is due to taking the first line only into consideration. Read together with the second line, *dvādaśasya* conveys no other

1 *IA.*, 1894, p. 243

2 B. states that J.'s assertion that the frogs reappear before the rains agrees with actualities in India. In this respect, he relates his own experience. The large species of the frog, the bull frog, makes the night hideous with its cries about a fortnight before the monsoon commences. He states that he will never forget his experience during the hot season of 1863, when he lived in the old Elphinstone College near the Gavāliā Talāo in Bombay. "During the latter half of May, the bull frogs came out every night and sitting round the tank, disturbed my sleep with the noises, which are described in so graphic a manner in the Frog hymn of the *Ṛgveda* and the corresponding verses of the *Atharvaveda*."

3 *IA.*, 1894, p. 244

4 *Ibid.*, p. 244

meaning than the twelfth. It is clearly stated that the year goes out (संवत्सरे)[1] and the rainy season begins (प्रावृष्यागतायां). It is as good as saying that the new year begins with the rains. It is idle to expect that in the early times of the Vedas, indication of year-beginning should be as explicit as today. It is only by implication that we understand that the *Ṛv.* mentions that there are 360 days in the year, there are 3, 5, 6 or 7 seasons and that the year was intercalated. It is therefore nothing strange that in the present case there is a mere hint of year-beginning in varṣā.

A translation of the 9th verse, *Ṛv.* VII. 103.

48. In order to make the meaning clear the verse may be translated as follows:—They protected (maintained) the order of the gods, therefore these persons do not disregard the time of the 12th month of the seasons. On the completion of the year and the appearance of the rainy season, the distressing heat comes to an end.

(4) Upākaraṇa

(Commencement of the Study of the Veda in each year)

Determination of the time of Upākaraṇa ceremony in ancient India (from the Sūtras).

49. J. states that in ancient India, the commencement of the study of the Veda coincided with the beginning of the rains. He says that in this regard the following information is supplied by the Sūtras:

According to the *Śāṅkhyāyana-Gṛhya-Sūtra* (4.5), the Upākaraṇa for the study of the Veda begins ओषधिनां प्रादुर्भावे (at the advent of the herbs). The *Gobhila-Gṛhya-Sūtra* (3.3) specifies the date as the full moon of Prauṣṭhapada (i.e. Bhādra) as well as that of Śrāvaṇa, which was "the first rainy month in Madhyadeśa in 2000 B.C."[2] The *Rāmāyāṇa*, III. 28. 54 refers to Prauṣṭhapada as the time for beginning the Vedic study.

J. points out that in the Sūtras, these and similar other references to the time for beginning the study of the Veda contain traces of a custom prevalent long before the period of the Sūtras. Apparently, the rains in Śrāvaṇa and Bhādra cannot refer to one and the same century. J. reconciles the two different months (Śrāvaṇa and Bhādra) for commencing the study of the Veda by showing that the Sūtras refer to the occurrence of the same event

1 It may also be rendered as 'at the end of the year'.

2 *IA.*, 1894, p. 155

in two different Nakṣatra epochs,[1] one being much earlier than the other. The importance of these references is emphasised by J., for he concludes that "an antiquated usage has been preserved down to the times, when the position of the heavenly bodies, and hence, the division of the months among the seasons of the year, have undergone alteration."[2]

How to explain the mention of different months by the Sūtras for beginning the study of the Veda.

50. It is concluded that the Schools in ancient India in particular Nakṣatra epochs opened *in the rainy season;* it implies that *that season* commenced with Śrāvaṇa in one epoch and with Bhādra in the preceding epoch.

The recession of one month is due to the lapse of time occupied by a Nakṣatra epoch. In fixing approximate length of time of the two epochs, two expressions viz. the 'sidereal year' and the 'tropical year' will be used. The 'sidereal year' is equivalent to the time required by the sun to move from a given star to the same star again, its mean value being 365 days, 6 hours, 9 minutes and 9·6 seconds. The 'tropical year' known also as 'astronomical', 'equinoctial', 'natural', or 'solar' year is equivalent to one complete circuit of the ecliptic by the sun, which is equal to 365 days, 5 hours, 48 minutes and 46 seconds.[3]

51. It will be seen that the difference between the sidereal year, and the tropical year, amounts to 20 minutes and 23·6 seconds, or 20·4 minutes, approximately. It is contended by T. that the year mentioned in the Vedic works was sidereal and not tropical. "This would necessitate a change in the beginning of the year, every two thousand years or so, to make it correspond with the cycle of natural seasons, and the fact that such changes were introduced twice or thrice is a further proof of the old year being a sidereal one. The difference between the sidereal and the tropical year is 20·4 minutes, which causes the seasons to fall back nearly one lunar month in approximately two thousand years, on an average, if the sidereal year be taken as the standard of measurement."[4]

1 Such as Mṛgaśiras epoch, Kṛttikā epoch.

2 *IA.*, 1894, p. 155

3 Chambers, *Twentieth Century Dictionary*, p. 1292:

The *tropical year* is the interval between the consecutive passages of the sun, through the same equinox or the same solstice.

The *sidereal year* is the interval between two consecutive passages of the sun, through a given fixed point of the ecliptic.

4 Tilak, *The Orion*, pp. 18, 19

It should only be pointed out that the ancient Indo-Aryan astronomers were unfamiliar with the terms 'tropical', or 'sidereal', But as their year was sidereal, they had to correct their calculation by changing the season by a month every two thousand years.

In the light of the above explanation, the difficulty in ascertaining the time for beginning the study of the Veda is expected to be overcome. According to the Nakṣatra epochs the first month in the rainy season may be Bhādra, Śrāvaṇa, or Āṣāḍha, in order of lesser and lesser antiquity of the related Nakṣatra epoch.

J. places the rainy season commencing in Śrāvaṇa in 2000 B.C. by computing according to his own Table. The rainy season in Bhādra would, therefore, fall in 4000 B.C. The Sūtra should be considered to refer to such times according to J.

The theory of Jacobi is rejected by Whitney ;

52. In discussing the implications of the passages of various Sūtras mentioned by J., W. endorses the principles underlying the above theory,[1] but rejects the idea that the indoor study of the Vedas, even if it be conceded that it began in the rainy season in 4000 B.C., must necessarily be attached to any particular month. He thinks that as the orthodox Vedic student had to go to school for a number of years, the month from which he began his study was immaterial, and also uncertain, depending as it did upon various factors like local conditions, climate etc.[2]

and also by Thibaut;

53. Th. also refers to the Sūtra passages dealt with by J. and dismisses J.'s inference by saying that he finds no sufficient reason for supporting the view that the isolated rule of some *Gṛhya-Sūtras* preserved remembrances of a period, as remote as 4000 B.C. He is at one with W. in attaching

1 W. has however indirectly admitted the truth of J.'s contention: "The seasons follow the equinoxes, and the solstices ; hence the rainy season, for example, began about a month earlier when Aśvinī (Arietis) was at equinox than when Kṛttikās (Pleiades) were there, and about two months earlier than when Mṛgaśiras (Orion) was there."—*IA*., 1895, p. 361

That difference of one month in the occurrence of the same event indicates a lapse of approximately 2000 years on average is also admitted thus by W: "'Pāraskara puts the initiation of the student at the full moon of the month Śrāvaṇa, which would have been the first month of the rains in the second millennium before Christ, while Gobhila sets it, alternately, in the month Bhādrapada, which would have occupied the same position more than two thousand years earlier or when the Vernal equinox was at Orion."

2 *IA*., 1895, p. 363

no importance to the month in which the study of the Vedas began.[1]

54. After making a close examination of several rules connected with sacred matters, B. concludes that they indicate that in ancient times, *Prauṣṭhapada* is the month in which summer solstice fell. B. states that both J. and T.[2] were struck by one set of such rules, viz. "those regarding the date of Upākaraṇa, or opening of the annual term of study." He further observes that "The Gṛhya [=G. S.] and Dharma Sūtras [=D. S.] state not merely that the solemn opening of the annual term happens on the appearance of the herbs, i.e., in the first days of the monsoon, when after the first heavy fall of the rains, the new vegetation springs up as if by magic. The monsoon bursts forth all over the Uttarāpatha, and in a large portion of the Dakṣiṇāpatha, exactly, or almost exactly, at the summer solstice.[3]

but fully suported by Bühler.

B. points out that though the appearance of the herbs should have fallen in a month corresponding to part of June, three different months are referred to by the sacred treatises, corresponding to June, July and August. He thinks that it was *Śrāvaṇa* which was mostly favoured for the Upākaraṇa ceremony.[4]

1 *IA.*, 1895, p. 96
In the opinion of Th., J. supposes "these two determinations [viz. Upākaraṇa in Śrāvaṇa and Bhādra] had been made at the times when the summer solstice, which marks the beginning of the rainy season, coincided with the full moon in Śrāvaṇa and Bhādrapada, respectively, i.e. about 2000 and 4000 B.C. The latter determination would thus belong to the same period, when the summer solstice was observed to take place in Phālguna. But these conclusions, if not supported by ample collateral evidence, are altogether precarious." *Ibid.*, pp. 95, 96

2 T. has not dealt with Upākaraṇa.

3 *IA*, 1894, p. 241

4 Bühler arranges the time for beginning the study of the Veda according to different sacred literatures as follows (*IA.*, 1894, p. 241).

(1) Āśvalāyana G.S. 3.5	On appearance of herb. Śrāvaṇa full moon or Hasta-day, Śrāvaṇa.
(2) Vasiṣṭha D.S. 13.1	Śrāvaṇa full moon. Prauṣṭhapada full moon.
(3) Pāraskara G.S. 2.10	Śrāvaṇa full moon or Hasta-day.
(4) Śāṅkvhāyana G.S. 4.5	On appearance of herb. Śrāvaṇa day or Hasta day.
(5) Yājñavalkya D.S. 1.142	On appearance of herb. Śrāvaṇa or Hasta-day.

A second date of the ceremony in the month of *Bhādra* is suggested by 5 *Gṛhya* and *Dharma Sūtras,* and also the Manu Smṛti, in addition to Śrāvaṇa. "The reason for citing this optional rule is, according to B., that optional rules in Vedic works not merely record ancient usages, which had become obsolete, but which the teachers did not like to omit, on account of their sanctity."[1]

Earliest date for the Upākaraṇa is 4000 B.C.

55. So, the earliest date for the Upākaraṇa ceremony may be fixed at not later than 4000 B.C., concludes B. It should be borne in mind that the study of the Vedas was a very important event in the life of the Indo-Aryans, as it was a saered duty of every citizen in the first of the Āśramas, the Brahmacarya. It is not likely that there was no fixed time for initiating this important phase of life of the Indo-Aryans. A little reflection will show that the contention that any month of a year was as good as another cannot be accepted. If the study of the Vedas, and with it the year, had been commenced haphazardly in different months it would have put the citizens of the country to a great inconvenience.[2]

(6) Mānava G.S.	Śrāvaṇa day in the rains.
(7) Mānava D.S. 4.95	Śrāvaṇa full moon—Bhādrapada full moon.
(8) Kāṭhaka G.S.	Śrāvaṇa day in the rains.
(9) Viṣṇu Smṛti 3.1	Śrāvaṇa full moon—Bhādrapada full moon.
(10) Baudhāyana G.S. 3.1.1 }	Āṣāḍha full moon.
(11) Baudhāyana D.S. 1.12.16 }	Śrāvaṇa full moon.
(12) Bhāradvāja G.S, 2.37	On appearance of herb. During Śrāvaṇa Pakṣa, Śrāvaṇa full moon.
(13) Āpastamba D.S. 1.9.1	Śrāvaṇa full moon.
(14) Hiraṇyakesa G.S. 2.18	During Śrāvaṇa Pakṣa Śrāvaṇa full moon.
(15) Vaikhānasa G.S. 2.12	Bright half of Āṣāḍha except 4th, 9th, and 14th.
(16) Gobhila G.S. 3.3	Śrāvaṇa full moon or Hasta-day.
(17) Khādira G.S. 3.2	Prauṣṭhapada (Bhādra) full moon.
(18) Gautama D.S. XVI. 1	Śrāvaṇa day in the rains.

1 *IA*, 1894, pp. 241, 242. The Upākaraṇa in Āṣāḍha must be a change over at a later date and is not discussed here.

2 Cf Keith, *Religion and Philosophy of the Veda and Upanishads*, 2, p. 137 Keith rejects B.'s conclusions without assigning any reason.

Frog Song (Rv. VII. 103) read with the Sūtras on Upākaraṇa, points to the earliest date of Upākaraṇa.

56. It is now apparent that the different dates indicated by the Sūtras[1] for beginning the study of the Vedas should not be taken as belonging to the same Nakṣatra epoch. As has been stated above, for each 2000 years, the Varṣā season recedes by one month in the order Bhādrapada, Śrāvaṇa, Āṣāḍha and so on.

In the last section, it was pointed out that the Frog Song of the *Rv.* (VII. 103) referred to the Varṣā year in some remote age, of which no time could be fixed.[2] Considered with what is stated here about the Upākaraṇa ceremony in Varṣā, the Vedic hymn must have been one of the subjects of reminiscences of the Sūtrakāras in their delineation of Upākaraṇa. As Śrāvauṇa Pūrṇimā was considered to be the most auspicious by many Sūtrakarās for commencing the Vedic study, the alternative date in Prauṣṭhapada must be considered to have been earlier, and placed in the Ṛgvedic times.

1 The *Gṛhya-Sūtras* were composed as formal treatises at a comparatively late Vedic period, but they report practices and prayers of great antiquity,—Bloomfield, the *Atharvaveda and the Gopatha-Brāhmaṇa*, Grundiss Series, p. 5, Oldenberg, SBE., pp. xvii ff,

2 See para 49.

Frog Song (Rv. VII. 103) read with the Sūtras on Upākaraṇa, points to the earliest date of Upākaraṇa.

56. It is now apparent that the different dates indicated by the Sūtras[1] for beginning the study of the Vedas should not be taken as belonging to the same Nakṣatra epoch. As has been stated above, for each 2000 years, the Varṣā season recedes by one month in the order Bhādrapada, Śrāvaṇa, Āṣāḍha and so on.

In the last section, it was pointed out that the Frog Song of the *Rv.* (VII. 103) referred to the Varṣā year in some remote age, of which no time could be fixed.[2] Considered with what is stated here about the Upākaraṇa ceremony in Varṣā, the Vedic hymn must have been one of the subjects of reminiscences of the Sūtrakāras in their delineation of Upākaraṇa. As Śrāvaṇa Pūrṇimā was considered to be the most auspicious by many Sutrakarās for commencing the Vedic study, the alternative date in Prauṣṭhapada must be considered to have been earlier, and placed in the Ṛgvedic times.

1 The *Gṛhya-Sūtras* were composed as formal treatises at a comparatively late Vedic period, but they report practices and prayers of great antiquity,—Bloomfield, the *Atharvaveda and the Gopatha-Brāhmaṇa,* Grundiss Series, p. 5, Oldenberg, SBE., pp. xvii ff.

2 See para 49.

(5) THE NAKṢATRA EPOCH IN VEDIC TIMES

1. The 'Sattra' or year-long Sacrifice

57. The Saṃvatsara Sattra or year-long sacrifice in the shape of *gavām ayana, ādityānām ayana, aṅgirasām ayana* etc. occupied a very important place in the life of the ancient Indo-Aryan people. This sacrifice has been elaborately described in the Saṃhitās and Brāhmaṇas like the *Taittirīya-Saṃhitā, Aitareya-Brāhmaṇa, Kauṣītaki-Brāhmaṇa.* T. states that there are sacrificial hymns in the *Ṛgveda* which bear evidence to a considerable development of the sacrificial ceremonies.[1] He further observes that these sacrifices were regulated by a calendar which was based on an intimate knowledge of months, seasons and year, and their connection with the heavenly bodies. This knowledge could not be acquired within a short time. Continued observation, for many years together, of the northern and southern courses of the sun, the changes in the seasons, the places of the sun and the moon in respect of particular Nakṣatras, etc. must have been carefully noted before certain conclusions were reached. It is now easy to criticise these conclusions after the lapse of so many centuries during which astronomy made much progress, but we must not overlook the great disadvantages under which those early astronomers had to work. They had neither laboratories nor instruments used by the present-day scientists. Yet they achieved results that do much credit to their intelligence.

The importance of Sattra in the life of the ancient Indo-Aryans.

Tilak states that year-long sacrifice had a close connection with the calendar.

58. In the second and third chapters of his *Orion*, T. has treated of Sattra, and the Nakṣatra Kṛttikā, while in the next three chapters, (IV, V, VI),[2] the Nakṣatra Mṛgaśiras has been dealt with. As the views contained in these chapters raised controversies amongst scholars, brief statements of their views are given below in the first instance, and afterwards they are examined.

Controversies raised by Tilak's views.

1 See Chapter 3, Antiquity of Sacrifice and Writing, in this essay.

2 The relevant chapters of the *Orion* are:

II Sacrifice *alias* the year (pp. 10-31).
III The Kṛttikās (pp. 32-60).
IV Agrahāyaṇa (pp. 61-95).
V The Antelope's Head (pp. 96-128).
VI Orion and his belt (pp. 129-156).

2. ANTIQUITY OF THE VEDA

1. *Opinions of Scholars*

A. Tilak's Arguments

Two main issues.

59. The two main questions that T. takes up are: (1) the meaning of the terms, Kṛttikā-series and Mṛgaśiras-series and whether they point to the antiquity of the Veda, and (2) the month from which the year-beginning was made in these early times.

60. While dealing with the Kṛttikās, T. uses two passages, one from the *Taittirīya-Saṃhitā*, VII. 4.8, and the other from the *Tāṇḍya-Brāhmaṇa*, V. 9, for establishing his theory. He quotes both the passages, translates the former one, omitting the *Tāṇḍya* passage as it is similar, in every respect, to the one quoted from the *Taitt. Saṃ.*

The two passages referred to above are as follows:

Text of the *Taittirīya-Saṃhitā* VII. 4.8.

संवत्सराय दीक्षिष्यमाणा एकाष्टकायां दीक्षेरन्नेषा वै संवत्सरस्य पत्नी यदेकाष्टकैतस्यां वा एष एतां रात्रिं वसति साक्षादेव संवत्सरमारभ्य दीक्षन्त आर्तं वा एते संवत्सरस्याभि दीक्षन्ते य एकाष्टकायां दीक्षन्तेऽन्तनामानावृतू भवतो व्यस्तं वा एते संवत्सरस्याभि दीक्षन्ते य एकाष्टकायां दीक्षन्तेऽन्तनामावृतू भवतः फल्गुनीपूर्णमासे दीक्षेरन् मुखं वा एतत् संवत्सरस्य यत् फल्गुनीपूर्णमासो मुखत एव संवत्सरमारभ्य दीक्षन्ते तस्यैकैव निर्या यत् साम्मेध्ये विषुवान् संपद्यते चित्रापूर्णमासे दीक्षेरन् मुखं वा एतत् संवत्सरस्य यच्चित्रापूर्णमासो मुखत एव संवत्सरमारभ्य दीक्षन्ते तस्य न काचन निर्या भवति चतुरहे पुरस्तात् पौर्णमास्यै दीक्षेरन् तेषामेकाष्टकायां क्रयः सं पद्यते तेनैकाष्टकां न संबट् कुर्वन्ति तेषां पूर्वपक्षे सुत्या सं पद्यते पूर्वपक्षं मासा अभि सं पद्यते ते पूर्वपक्ष उत्तिष्ठन्ति तानुत्तिष्ठत ओषधयो वनस्पतयोऽनूत्तिष्ठन्ति तान् कल्याणी कीर्तिरनूत्तिष्ठत्यरात्सुरिमे यजमाना इति तदनु सर्वे राध्नुवन्ति ।

Text of the *Tāṇḍya-Br.*

एकाष्टकायां दीक्षेरन् ॥१

एषा वै संवत्सरस्य पत्नी यदेकाष्टकैतस्यां वा एतां रात्रिं वसति साक्षादेव तत् संवत्सरमारभ्य दीक्षन्ते ॥२

तस्य सा निर्या यदपोऽनभिनन्दन्तोऽभ्यवयन्ति ॥३

विच्छिन्नं वा एते संवत्सरस्याभिदीक्षन्ते य एकाष्टकायां दीक्षन्तेऽकृतनामानावृतू भवतः ॥४

आर्तें वा एते संवत्सरस्याभि दीक्षन्ते येऽन्तनामानावृतू अभि दीक्षन्ते ॥५

तस्मादेकाष्टकायां न दीक्ष्यम् ॥६

फाल्गुने दीक्षेरन् ॥७

मुखं वा एतत् संवत्सरस्य यत् फाल्गुनी मुखत एव तत् संवत्सरमारभ्य दीक्षन्ते ॥८

तस्य सा निर्या यत् सम्मेघे विषुवान् संपद्यते ॥९

चित्रापूर्णमासे दीक्षेरन् ॥१०

चक्षुर्वा एतत् संवत्सरस्य यच्चित्रापूर्णमासो मुखतो वै चक्षुर्मुखत एव तत् संवत्सरमारभ्य दीक्षन्ते तस्य न निर्यास्ति ॥११

चतुरहे पुरस्तात् पौर्णमास्या दीक्षेरन् ॥१२

तेषामेकाष्टकायां क्रयः संपद्यते तेनैकाष्टकां न संवट् कुर्वन्ति ॥१३

तेषां पूर्वपक्षे सुत्या संपद्यते पूर्वपक्षे मासाः संतिष्ठमाना यन्ति पूर्वपक्ष उत्तिष्ठन्ति तानुत्तिष्ठतः पशव ओषधयोऽनूत्तिष्ठन्ति तान् कल्याणी वागभिवदत्यरात्सुरिमे सत्रिण इति ते राध्नुवन्ति ॥१४

61. I reproduce below T.'s rendering of the *Taittirīya-Saṃhitā* passage,

Tilak's translation of the passage from the Taittirīya-Saṃhitā.

"Those who are about to consecrate themselves for the year (sacrifice) should do so on the Ekāshṭakā (day). The Ekāshṭakā is the wife of the year ; and he [i.e., the year] lives in her [i.e., the Ekāshṭakā] for that night. (Therefore they) practically sacrifice (by) beginning the year. Those that sacrifice on the Ekāshṭakā, sacrifice to the distressed (period) of the year. It is the season (*dual*) whose name comes last. Those, that sacrifice on the Ekāshṭakā, sacrifice to the reversed (period) of the year. It is the season (*dual*) whose name comes last. They should consecrate themselves for the sacrifice on the Phalgunī full-moon. The Phalgunī full-moon is the mouth of the year. They sacrifice (by) beginning the year from the very mouth, It has only one fault, *viz.*, that the Vishūvān [i.e., the equator or the central day] falls in the rains. They should consecrate them-

Ekāṣṭakā.

Phalgunī full-moon.

1 *The Orion*, pp. 44, 45

selves for the sacrifice on the Chitrā full-moon. The Chitrā full-moon is the mouth of the year. They sacrifice (by) beginning the year from the very mouth. It has no fault whatsoever. They should consecrate themselves for the sacrifice four days before the full-moon. Their *Kraya* [i.e., the purchase of Soma] falls on the Ekāshṭakā. Thereby they do not render the Ekāshṭakā void [i.e., of no consequence]. Their *Sutyā* [i.e., the extraction of Soma juice] falls in the first [i.e., the bright] half (of the month). Their months [i.e., the monthly sacrifices] fall in the first half. They rise [i.e., finish their sacrifice] in the first half. On their rising, herbs and plants rise after them. After them rises the good fame that these sacrifices have prospered. Thereon all prosper."[1]

Citrā full-moon.

4 days before the full-moon

62. The above passage, read with the *Tāṇḍya-Brāhmaṇa*, V. 9, indicates different times for beginning the year-long Sattra. They are :

The different times of the commencement of Sattra, and their signification.

I. The first is the Ekāṣṭakā day. In explaining its meaning T. refers to *Āśvalāyana-Gṛhya-Sūtra*, II. 4. 1—हेमन्तशिशिरयोश्चतुर्णामपरपक्षाणामष्टमीष्वष्टकाः—which denotes that the term is used for the 8th day of the latter (dark) half of the four months of Hemanta and Śiśira seasons.[2] He does not however forget to point out that sometimes it denotes the 8th day of the dark half of each of the 12 months in the year, as in द्वादशैकाष्टकाः द्वादशामावास्याः ॥ (*Tāṇḍya-Br.*, X. 3. 11). He further states that in commenting on the *Tāṇḍya-Brāhmaṇa*, V. 9, Sāyaṇa observes that the word Ekāṣṭakā is used there in the secondary sense, and quotes *Āpastamba-Gṛhya-Sūtra*, VIII. 21. 10 (या माघ्या पौर्णमास्या उपरिष्टाद्व्यष्टका तस्याष्टमी ज्येष्ठया सम्पद्यते । तामेकाष्टकेत्याचक्षते ।) and that both Jaimini and Āpastamba interpret it to mean the 8th day of the dark half of Māgha (Śiśira), i.e., the particular day which the Mīmāṃsakas understand by Ekāṣṭakā. T. concludes that Ekāṣṭakā is practically the 'constructive beginning' of the year, and the year-long sacrifice may be commenced on that day.[3]

I Ekāṣṭakā, and its meaning.

1 *The Orion*, pp. 46, 47 2 *Ibid.*, p. 47 3 *Ibid.*, p. 48

Three objections against Ekāṣṭakā.

There are however three objections to the commencement of the sacrifice on Ekāṣṭakā day as pointed out in the above quoted passage. T. enumerates them thus.

The day falls (a) in distressed period of the year;

(a) The 8th day of the dark half of Māgha falls in the distressed (आर्त) period of the year. Following Śabara and other commentators, T. takes this distress to be due to cold, and points out that though Sāyaṇa's interpretation of the words is different (implying according to him that the old year is brought to an end), yet both Sāyaṇa and Śabara agree that in those days, the year ended before the 8th day of the dark half of Māgha.[1]

(b) in the last season;

(b) The day falls in the last season. In explaining how it can be in the last season, T. states that though Ekāṣṭakā marks the beginning of the year, it is nonetheless in the last season of the year, for it is continuation of the last season of the previous year ended on the 7th day of the dark half of the month of Māgha. The difficulty created by the use of the word ऋतु in dual (dvi-vacana) in the passage is removed by T. by a reference to *Taitt.-Saṃ.*, IV. 11. 1. and *Vājasaneyi-Saṃ.*, 13-25, where also the word is used in dual implying two months constituting the season (like the word scissors in English) to denote singular number—द्विवचनमेकवचनार्थम् । (Mahīdhara).[2]

(c) in a reversed period of the year.

(c) To commence sacrifice on the Ekāṣṭakā day is to sacrifice to the reversed व्यस्त period of the year, because the sun then turns away from the winter solstice. T. points out that according to Śabara this indicates the change of *ayanas*, and that this opinion is endorsed by Sāyaṇa.[3]

II Phalgunī full-moon.

63. II. The second is Phalgunī full-moon day which gets over the above three objections. It was known as the first day of the year. By sacrificing on this day, one avoids the difficulties encountered in the case of Ekāṣṭakā and still sacrifices at the beginning of the year. (मुखं वा एतत् वत्सरस्य). This has however one fault, *viz.* that if

1 *Ibid.*, pp. 48, 49

2 *Ibid.*, pp. 49, 50

3 *Ibid.*, p. 50

It may be noted here that according to T. it seems that Śabara quotes from the *Tāṇḍya-Brāhmaṇa* where it clearly states the first objection as follows: "not delighted with water they go to *avabhṛtha* (i.e., the final bath.)"

sacrifice commences on Phalgunī full-moon day, the middle or central day, i.e., the Viṣuvat falls in the rainy season, which is not a desirable time. T. explains how the Viṣuvat falls in the rainy season thus: the first 12 days are devoted to consecration and twelve more to *Upasads*, after which the sacrifice proper commences. So the Viṣuvat falls after 6 months and 24 days from Phalgunī full-moon, i.e., 'on the 9th of the bright half of the month of Āśvina' (Sāyaṇa). If winter solstice or beginning of cold season should fall on the Māgha full-moon, the summer solstice or the end of the summer and the beginning of the rainy season would fall a little after the full moon in Śrāvaṇa (or Bhādra). Therefore, the months of Bhādra and Āśvina represented the rainy season at the time referred to in the *Taitt.-Saṃ.*, and the Viṣuvat in the rainy season was not auspicious.[1]

One objection : the Viṣuvat falls in the rainy season.

III Citrā full-moon (faultless).

64. III. The third is the Citrā full-moon, which was faultless and open to no objection.[2]

IV 4 days before the full-moon.

65, IV. The fourth is 4 days before the full-moon. There is no specific mention of the month to which this full-moon is to be attached. It may mean

(a) any full-moon day in the year, as Ekāṣṭakā may mean the 8th day of the dark half of any month in the year, though it has the special sense of being the 8th day of the dark half of Māgha ;

(b) the Citrā full-moon which is mentioned immediately before in the same passage ;

(c) the Māgha full-moon as Ekāṣṭakā is mentioned immediately afterwards.[3]

In one of the Adhikaraṇas, Jaimini discusses the subject and decides in favour of the full-moon in the month of Māgha.[4]

1 Tilak, *The Orion, p.* 51 2 *Ibid.*, p. 51 3 *Ibid.*, pp. 51, 52

4 *Ibid.*, p. 52:

1. पौर्णमास्यामनियमोऽविशेषात् ।
2. आनन्तर्यात्तु चत्री स्यात् ।
3. माघो वकाष्टकाश्रुतेः ।
4. अन्या अपीति चेत् ।
5. न भक्तित्वादेषा हि लोके ।
6. दीक्षापराधे चानुग्रहात् ।
7. उत्थाने चानुप्ररोहात् ।
8. अस्यां च सर्वलिङ्गानि ।

Jaimini-Sūtras, VI. 5. 30-37 (as quoted by T.)

Jaimini states that those who sacrifice on this full-moon day can purchase their Soma on the Ekāṣṭakā which is no other than the one mentioned in the beginning, and that the full-moon must, therefore, be the one next preceding this Ekāṣṭakā. When the sacrifice is finished, the herbs and plants spring up, which can happen only in the Vasanta season according to Śabara.[1]

66. Jaimini's interpretation of this part of the passage leads T. to deduce the following conclusions:

Tilak accepts the meaning attributed to it by the Mīmāṃsakas, *viz.* 4 days before the full-moon of Māgha.

(a) In the days in the *Taittirīya-Saṃhitā*, the winter solstice occurred before the 8th day of the dark half of Māgha. Whether the solstitial day fell on the Māgha full-moon is difficult to say, priests not selecting a day in the reversed period of the year. The choice of a day before the full-moon in Māgha clearly indicates that solstice occurred on that day. So, the full-moon in Māgha was one of the beginnings.[2]

(b) The year commenced with winter solstice.[3]

(c) "As there cannot be three real beginnings of the year at the interval of one month each, the passage must be understood as recording a tradition about the Chitrā full-moon and the Phalgunī full-moon being once considered as the first days of the year."[4]

(d) Viṣuvat lost its primary meaning and fell in the rainy season when the sacrifice commenced in Phalgunī full-moon.[5]

67. These conclusions lead T. to affirm that confirmatory and direct evidence "of the coincidence of the Kṛttikās with the vernal equinox in the days of" the *Taittirīya-Saṃhitā* has been found.

Proof of the coincidence of Kṛttikās with vernal equinox.

T. states that independently of the *Vedāṅga-Jyotiṣa*, there are four different statements in the *Taittirīya-Saṃhitā* and *Tāṇḍya-Brāhmaṇa* clearly showing that the vernal equinox was then in the Kṛttikās, *viz.*

(1) The *Taittirīya-Saṃhitā* and the *Tāṇḍya-Brāhmaṇa* give lists of Nakṣatras, and their presiding deities always with the Kṛttikā at the beginning[6];

(2) The *Taittirīya-Saṃhitā* has an express statement that the Kṛttikās are the mouth of the Nakṣatras;[7]

(3) the passage quoted above tells us that winter solstice fell in the month of Māgha;[8]

1 Tilak, *The Orion*, p. 52
2 *Ibid.*, pp. 53, 54
3 *Ibid.*, p. 54
4 *Ibid.*, p. 54
5 *Ibid.*, p. 54
6 *Ibid.*, p. 54
7 *Ibid.*, p. 54
8 *Ibid.*, pp. 54, 55

(4) it is stated that the Kṛttikās are the mouth of the Deva Nakṣatras, i.e., Nakṣatras in the northern hemisphere above the vernal equinox.[1]

According to T., there is enough evidence "to establish the proposition that the Kṛittikās coincided with the vernal equinox, when the *Taittirīya-Saṃhitā* was compiled."[2] The time of compilation of the *Taittirīya-Saṃhitā* is determined by T. to be 2350[3] B.C. by a reference to W.'s calculation.[4]

The signification of winter solstice in Māgha.

68. T. states that in those days Māgha and Phālguna were comprised in Śiśira, and Caitra and Vaiśākha in Vasanta. As evidence, T. cites several instances from the *Brāhmaṇas* and the *Sūtras*, which indicate that the full-moon night in the month of Phālguna is the first night of the year.

Different texts regarding beginning of the year in Phālguna.

'The Phalgunī full-moon is the first night of the year.' – the *Śatapatha-Brāhmaṇa*[5].

The *Taittirīya*[6] and *Śāṅkhāyana*[7]*-Brāhmaṇas* contain similar passages.

The *Gopatha Brāhmaṇa*,[8] after stating that the Uttarā and Pūrvā Phalgunī are respectively the beginning and the end of the year,

1 *Ibid.*, p. 55 2 *Ibid.*, p. 55

3 3000 B.C. according to his *Arctic Home.*

4 *Sūrya Siddhānta*, add. notes, p. 328

5 एषा ह संवत्सरस्य प्रथमा रात्रिर्यत् फाल्गुनी पौर्णमासी योत्तरैषोत्तमा या पूर्वा मुखत एव तत् संवत्सरमारभते ।

VI. 2. 2. 18 [Tilak, *The Orion*, p. 67 fn.]

And furthermore, at the Phālguna (full-moon), for the full-moon of Phālguna, that is, the second (Phālguna), is the first night of the year: and that first (Phālguna) is the last (night of the year): he then begins the year at the very mouth (beginning). —Eggeling (tr.), *Śat. Br.*, pt. III, p. 179

6 एषा वै प्रथमा रात्रिः संवत्सरस्य यदुत्तरे फल्गुनी । मुखत एव संवत्सरस्याग्निमाधाय बलीयान् भवति । I. 1. 2. 8. [Tilak, *The Orion*, p. 67 fn.]

Uttarā Phalgunī is the first night of the year. One becomes rich by consecrating the fire at the mouth of the year.

7 मुखं वा एतत् संवत्सरस्य यत् फाल्गुनी पौर्णमासी

IV. 4 [Tilak, *The Orion*, p. 67 fn.].

The Phalgunī full-moon is the mouth of the year.

8 मुखमुत्तरे फल्गुन्यौ पुच्छं पूर्वे । तद् यथा प्रवृत्तस्यान्तौ समेतौ स्यातमेवमेतत् संवत्सरस्यान्तौ समेतौ भवत । II. I. 19 [Tilak, *The Orion*, p. 67fn. [.

adds: "just as the two ends of a thing meet so these two termini of the year meet together".

The Sūtra writers, though not so explicit, distinctly state that year-long sacrifices "should be commenced either on the Citrā or the Phālgunī full-moon night", indicating thereby the beginning of the year.[1]

These examples prompt T. to conclude that "If these passages mean anything, we must hold that the Phālgunī full-moon night was once considered to be actually the *first* night of the year, or to put it in a modern form the new year's night."[2]

The fact that the Māghī, the Phālgunī and the Caitrī full-moons "are mentioned together in the *same* passage of the *Taittirīya-Saṃhitā*, and for the *same* purpose" impels T. to conclude that the real meaning of the passage in the *Taitt. Saṃ.* and the passages in the *Brāhmaṇas* must be understood to be that with the full-moon the year commenced at the winter solstice for the purpose of year-long sacrifice.[3]

According to Tilak the *Taitt. Saṃ.* refers to an older year-beginning.

69. T. states that in the above-quoted passage of the *Taitt. Saṃ.* there is a reference to an older year beginning,—"the full moon in Phālguna did as a matter of fact once commence the year at the winter solstice,"[4]

This was so, says T., after the priests changed their mouth (starting point) of the Nakṣatras to Kṛttikās (from Mṛgaśiras). They however continued to recognise and record in the texts the Nakṣatra Mṛgaśiras as the mouth of the preceding series for the preceding Nakṣatra epoch and that for sacrificial purposes.[5]

One objection to the above-mentioned view may be put thus: To admit that the Hindus knew of an earlier Nakṣatra series with

In Uttarā Phalgunī is the beginning, and in Pūrvā Phalgunī the end (of the year). Just as the two ends of a thing meet, so these two termini of the year meet together. [Tilak, *The Orion*, p. 67]

1 तेषां (सांवत्सरिकाणां) फाल्गुन्यां पौर्णमास्यां चैत्र्यां वा प्रयोगः । *Āśvalāyana-Śr.-Sū.* I. 2.14. 3; *Kāt. Śr. Sū.* V. 1. 1; *Sān. Śr. Sū.* III. 8. 1, XIII. 18.3 [Tilak, *The Orion*, p. 67 fn.]

2 Tilak, *The Orion*, p. 68

3 *Ibid.*, p. 69

4 *Ibid.*, p. 70

5 *Ibid.*, p. 70: "......the old priests, after changing their starting point to Kṛttikās and framing the calendar accordingly, continued to recognize for sacrificial purposes, the older positions of the Nakṣatras."

Mṛgaśiras as the mouth is to indicate that the time of the Vedic works is to be pushed back another 2000 years. Therefore, that view is unacceptable to those scholars who think that Mṛgaśiras series was unknown to the Indo-Aryans of the time.

T. however thinks that the Vedas contain sufficient evidence in favour of the familiarity of the Indo-Aryans with the Nakṣatra series with Mṛgaśiras at their head. According to him, it can be gathered from the *Brāhmaṇas* that the texts speak of year beginning with Phālgunī full-moon, with which winter solstice coincided. Therefore, if in the commencement of the year there is a recession of one month, *viz.* from Phālguna to Māgha the vernal equinox must also have receded from Mṛgaśiras to Kṛttikās according to the principle that the lapse of each 2000 years brought about a recession of one month or of 2¼ Nakṣatras on an average.[1]

The Vedic year never commenced with Mārgaśīrṣa or Agrahāyaṇa, according to Tilak.

70. T. considers the notion, that in old times the year once commenced with the month of Mārgaśirṣa or Agrahāyaṇa, to be a prevalent common error. He deals with this question at some length in his chapter on 'Agrahāyaṇa'[2] and concludes that only two beginnings of the year were known to ancient Indo-Aryan literature:—1) from Phālguna (winter solstice), the Nakṣatra being Mṛgaśiras (which T. equates with Agrahāyaṇa), and 2) from Māgha (winter solstice), the Nakṣatra being Kṛttikās (which was the mouth of the Nakṣatra series). In both the cases the year commenced from the vernal equinox.[3]

B. Jacobi's Arguments

Jacobi on year-beginning.

71. J. has treated the year-beginning a little differently from T. It has already been pointed out that J. finds, in the Frog Song (*Rv.*, VII. 103) and in Upākaraṇa (mentioned in the Dharma and Gṛhya Sūtras)[4], a reference to the year-beginning in the rainy season (Varṣā) in early Vedic times. As to the month with which this season began at that time, J. states that "The full moon in Bhādrapada belongs to the summer solstice in Phalgunī; the first rainy month was therefore Bhādrapada or Praushṭhapada, since the summer

1 *Ibid.*, pp. 71, 72
2 *Ibid.*, pp. 61-95 3 *Ibid.*, p. 89
4 See paras 43-48, and 49-56

solstice coincided...with the beginning of the rainy season."[1] Further, "The opening of the schools, therefore, in Praushṭhapada appears to go back to earliest times of the *Rig-veda*, for even then it is likely there was an official scholastic year, in which the sacred science was communicated orally."[2]

Varṣā year.

J. thus finds that "an antiquated usage [Upākaraṇa] has been preserved down to times when the position of the heavenly bodies, and hence, the division of the months among the seasons of the year, have undergone alteration."[3] He therefore expects to find similar traces of change in the more modern Vedic works.[4] Extensive searches convince him that Kṛttikā is almost always the first in order of Nakṣatras in later Vedic works. For instance, the *Kauṣītaki-Br.*, V. 1, has "*ūttare phalgū* form the beginning (*mukham*), while the *pūrve phalgū* form the tail (*puccham*) of the year"; and the *Taitt.-Br.*, I. 1. 2. 8 : "the *pūrve phālgunī* is called the last night, *jaghanyā rātriḥ*, the *ūttare phālgunī*, on the other hand, is called the first night of the year."[5] These indicate, states J., more exactly that there was an older Vedic period, tradition of which is kept up here, when the colure passed through Uttara Phalgunī: and it must not be taken as contemporary testimony."[6]

Hīmā year.

72. J. then goes on to deal with the probability of prevalence of two other dates for the beginning of the year. He states that the counter-part of the Varṣā year (which began with a summer solstice), was the Himā year beginning six months earlier [than the previous one] with winter solstice, the first month of which would be Phālguna. J. cites the following in support of his statement :

मुखं वा एतत् संवत्सरस्य यत् फल्गुनीपूर्णमासः ।

Taitt. Saṃ., VII. 4, 8, 1-2[7]

मुखं वा एतत् संवत्सरस्य यत् फाल्गुनः ।

Pañcaviṃśa Br., V. 9. 9[8]

73. The third kind of year was the Śarad year, states J., simply mentioned as Śarad in the *Ṛgveda*. Such a year began

1-3 *IA*, 1894, p. 155

4 *Ibid.*, p. 156 5 *Ibid.*, pp. 155. 156 6 *Ibid.*, p. 156

7 What is phalgunī full-moon is the mouth of this the year.

8 What is phālguna is the mouth of this the year.

with autumnal equinox or with full moon nearest to the same.[1]

Śarad year.

J. finds himself corroborated by the fact that the first month of the Śarad year is Agrahāyaṇa (meaning 'belonging to the beginning of the year') which is same as Mārgaśīrṣa. "As at that time Mṛigaśiras denoted the vernal equinox, it follows that the autumnal full moon must occur in conjunction with the same sign and that the first month must be Mārgaśiras."[2]

Three sorts of year.

74. The three sorts of years pointed out by J. have the following initial months for the three divisions of 4 months each,—Caturmāsyāni ṛtumukhāni:

Himā year month	Śarad year month	Varṣā year month
I. Phālguna (12th) portion in previous year.	II. Caitra (1st)	III. Vaiśākha (2nd)
II. Āṣāḍha (4th)	III. Śrāvaṇa (5th)	I. Pra-uṣṭhapada (6th)
III. Kārtika (8th)	I. Mārgaśīrṣa (9th)	II. Pauṣa (10th)[3]

In explaining the apparent contradiction in Vedic statements about the Cāturmāsya ceremony, "inasmuch as all the above three lists are recorded as existing side by side," J. is impelled to conclude that these periods of 4 months cannot be references to actual seasons, for he thinks it to be impossible that within a single period, even if extended to 1000 years or more, one season could have begun in three successive months. "The contradiction, however, disappears if we assume that the division of the year current at the epoch of the *Ṛig-veda*, the three kinds of year which have been proved to exist before, were in later times retained for liturgical purposes."[4]

75. J. is satisfied that, "These combinations point,...without a possibility of error, to a position of the colures, such as we have given for the oldest period, that of the *Ṛig-veda*. The later Vedic period introduced a correction, consisting in the transference of the opening point of the year from Mṛigaśiras to Kṛittikā; and it is precisely this circumstance that gives a material significance to the determination,

The solution of the contradiction in admitting the existence of different year-beginnings at the same time.

1 "Now at the time in which the summer solstice was in Uttara-Phalgunī, and the winter solstice was in Pūrva-Bhādrapadā, the autumnal equinox was in Mūla, and the vernal equinox was in Mṛigaśiras."—*IA.*, 1894, p. 156

2-3 *IA*, 1894, p. 156

4 *Ibid.*, pp. 156, 157

for it must have been approximately correct for the time of the correction."[1]

Tables of Nakṣatras by Jacobi point to 3000 B.C. to 2000 B.C. as the time when vernal equinox was in the Kṛttika.

76. The tables of Nakṣatras on the basis of the *Sūrya Siddhānta,* edited by W., p. 211, are appended by J. to his article.[2] They are reproduced here. A reference to them shows that the vernal equinox was in the Kṛttikā, and the summer solstice in Ṁaghā about 2500 B.C. J. admits the possibility of an error of five centuries on the part of these early astronomers, so that the period may lie between 3000 and 2000 B.C. In this connection he rejects the evidence of the *Vedāṅga-Jyotiṣa,* as he thinks that it belongs to a much later date, say, 14th or 15th century B.C.[3]

The Vedic texts contain a determination of colures true for 4500 B.C.

77. J. therefore holds that his chief thesis has been proved. "The Vedic texts, properly so called, contain a determination of the colures, which was evidently correct for them, and was only corrected in the *Jyotisha,* a determination that leads us to at least the beginning, of the three thousand years B.C. Considerably older than this, even, is the position of the colures, which we may infer for the *Rig-Veda,* a position which, as our table shews, corresponded to reality about 4500 B.C."[4]

J. states that the *Ṛgveda,* as a mature product, may belong to a later date, but he refers to the civilization as extending from about 4500 to 2500 B.C., in the second half of which is to be placed the collection of hymns as they have come down to us.

1 *Ibid.,* p. 157 2 *Ibid.,* p. 159

3-4 *Ibid.,* p. 157

Longitudes of Principal Stars of the Nakṣtras at various times

No.	Name	560 A.D.	0 B.C.	1000 B.C.	2000 B.C.	3000 B.C.	4000 B.C.	Name of Stars
27	Aśvinī	13·93°	6·70°	353·83°	341·04°	328·31°	315·64°	Arietis
28	Bharaṇī	26·90	19·67	6·80	354·01	341·28	327·61	Muscae
1	Kṛttikā	39·97	32·74	19·87	7·08	354·35	341·68	Tauri
2	Rohiṇī	49·75	42·52	29·65	16·86	4·13	350·46	Aldebaran
3	Mṛgaśiras	63·67	56·44	43·57	30·78	18·05	5·38	Orionis
4	Ārdrā	68·71	61·48	48·61	35·82	22·09	9·42	Beteigeuze
5	Punarvasu	93·23	86·00	73·13	60·34	47·61	34·94	Pollux
6	Puṣya	108·70	101·47	88·60	75·81	63·08	50·41	Cancri
7	Aśleṣā	112·33	105·10	92·23	79·44	66·71	54 04	Hydrae
8	Maghā	129·81	122·58	109·71	96·92	84·19	71·52	Regulus
9	Pūrva Phalgunī	141·25	134·02	121·15	108·36	95·63	82·96	Leonis

No.	Name	560 A.D.	0 B.C.	1000 B. C.	2000 B.C.	3000 B.C.	4000 B.C.	Name of Stars
10	Uttara Phalgunī	151·61	144·38	131·51	118·72	105·99	93·32	Leonis
11	Hasta	173·45	166·22	153·35	140·56	127·83	115·16	Corvi
12	Citrā	183·81	176·58	163·71	150·92	137·19	125·52	Spica
13	Svātī	184·20	176·97	164·10	151·31	138·58	125·91	Arcturus
14	Viśākhā	211·00	203·77	190·90	178·11	165·38	152·71	Librae
15	Anurādhā	222·57	215·34	202·47	189·68	176·95	164·28	Scorpionis
16	Jyeṣṭhā	229·73	222·50	209·63	196·84	183·11	171·44	Antares
17	Mūla	244·55	237·32	224·45	211·66	198·93	186·26	Scorpionis
18	P. Āṣāḍhā	254·53	247·30	234·43	221·64	208·91	196·24	Sagittariu
19	U. Āṣāḍhā	262·35	255·12	242·25	229·46	216·73	203·06	,,
20	Abhijit	265·25	258·02	245·15	232·36	219·63	206·96	Vega
21	Śravaṇā	281·68	274·45	261·58	248·79	236·06	223·39	Atair
22	Śraviṣṭhā	296·31	289·08	276·21	263·42	250·69	238·02	Delphini
23	Śatabhiṣaj	321·25	314·32	301·45	288·66	275·93	263·26	Aquarii
24	P. Bhādrapadā	333·45	326·22	313·35	300·56	287·83	275·16	Pegasi
25	U. Bhādrapadā	349·13	341·90	329·03	316·24	303·51	290·84	Andromedae
26	Revatī	359·83	352·60	339·73	326·93	314·21	301·54	Piscium

Supplementary Tables

I		II	
Degrees	Years	Years	Degrees
1°	78	100	1.28°
2	156	200	2.56
3	234	300	3.84
4	312	400	5.12
5	390	500	6.40
6	469	600	7.68
7	547	700	8.96
8	625	800	10.24
9	703	900	11.52
10	781	1000	12.80
11	859		
12	937		

Note—This table is based on that given by Whitney in the *Sūrya-Siddhānta*, for A.D. 560. The precession has been calculated according to Bessel. The supplementary Tables serve to determine approximately (i) the longitude for the intervals between the dates mentioned in the large table, and (2) the periods for longitudes not mentioned.[1]

C. Whitney's Arguments

Criticism of the Views of Jacobi and Tilak

78. W. introduces his subject[2] by stating that J. and also T.[3] arrived at an accordant conclusion, *viz.* that "the oldest period called Vedic goes back to or into the fifth millennium before Christ—an antiquity as remote as that long recognized for Egyptian civilization, and recently claimed, on good grounds, for that of Mesopotamia also." He calls this a startling novelty; but does not reject the conclusion outright, and demands distinct and unequivocal evidence in its favour before he accepts it.[4]

Whitney states that the fixing of age of the *Ṛgveda* in the 5th millennium B.C. is a startling novelty.

1 *IA.*, 1894, p. 159

2 "On a recent attempt, by Jacobi and Tilak, to determine on astronomical evidence the date of the Earliest Vedic Period as 4000 B.C".—*IA.*, 1895, pp. 361-369

3 *IA.*, 1895, p. 365

4 *Ibid.*, p. 361

The general argument of Jacobi and Tilak as summarised by Whitney.

79. He then goes on to make an elaborate survey of the views of J. and T. item by item, but before doing that he puts the general argument of the two scholars briefly thus:

"The Hindus (as also the Chinese, the Persians, and the Arabs) had a lunar zodiac of 27 (or 28) asterisms, rudely marking the successive days of the moon's circuit of the heavens, Since the establishment of the Hindu science of astronomy, under Greek influence and instruction, in the first centuries of our era, the series of asterisms has been made to begin with Aśvinī (in the head of Aries), for the acknowledged reason that that group was nearest the vernal equinox at the time. But earlier, in the *Brāhmaṇas*, etc., the series always began with Kṛittikā (Pleiades), presumably because, owing to the precession, that group had been nearest to the equinox: and this was the case some two thousand and more years before Christ. Some two thousand and more years yet earlier, the equinox was near to the Mṛigaśiras or the head of Orion; if, therefore, it can be made to appear that the Hindus once began their asterismal system with Mṛigaśiras and because of the latter's coincidence with the equinox, we shall conclude that they must have done so more than four thousand years before Christ. But the same sum can be worked in terms of months. The Hindu months are lunar, and are named sidereally, each from the asterism in or adjacent to which the moon is full in the given month: but the seasons follow the equinoxes and solstices; hence, the rainy season, for example, began about a month earlier when Aśvinī (Aries) was at the equinox than when Kṛittika (Pleiades) was there, and about two months earlier than when Mṛigaśiras (Orion) was there; and if it can be shown that the year always commenced with a fixed season[1], and has twice changed[2] its initial month[3], [then] Mṛigaśiras (Orion) will thus also be proved to have been at the equinox at a recorded or remembered period in Hindu history. And this, in one of the two alternative methods, or in both combined, is what our two authors attempt to demonstrate."[4]

(A) Whitney on Jacobi's Views

80. W. then examines the theory of year-beginning as propounded by J. and T. The former discovers the existence of a

1 (consisting of 2 months)

2 Once when the Mṛgaśiras series began and after that, when the Kṛttikā series began.

3 [of the season consisting of 2 months]

4 *IA.*, 1895, pp. 361-362

Varṣā year in Vedic times from the mention of frogs in Frog-song (*Ṛv., VII.* 103),[1] and of Upākaraṇa, i.e., commencement of the study of the Veda in the Sūtras.[2] W. denies that *Ṛv.*, VII. 103. 9, on which J. depends, establishes unequivocally the Varṣā year[3]. Nor is he convinced that the Sūtrakāras intended to attach the commencement of the study of the Veda to any particular month.[4]

Whitney does not think that Frog-song (*Ṛv., VII.* 103) or the Upākaraṇa ceremony indicates a Varṣā-year in Vedic times

As regards J.'s statement on the connection established by several of the *Brāhmaṇas* between the two Phalgunīs and the beginning and end of the year, W. makes use of the following Vedic texts.

Whitney examines whether the two Phalgunīs indicate the beginning and end of the year.

The *Taittirīya-Saṃhīta,* VII. 4. 8 and the *Pañcaviṃśa-Brāhmaṇa,* V. 9. 8 "say simply that 'the full-moon in Phalgunī is the mouth (*mukha,* i. e., beginning) of the year'; this would imply a position of the sun near the western of the two Bhādrapadas (Pegasi, etc), and determine the Phālguna month, beginning 14 days earlier, as the first month."[5]

The *Kauṣītaki-Brāhmaṇa,* V. I makes an almost identical statement with an addition that "the latter (eastern) Phalgu's are the mouth, the former (western) are the tail."[6]

The *Taittirīya-Brāhmaṇa,* I.6.2 virtually comments on the above when it says that "the former Phalgunī's are the last night of the year, and the latter Phalgunī's are the first night of the year."[7]

The *Śatapatha-Brāhmaṇa,* VI. 2.2.18 gives a little different version thus: "The full-moon of Phalgunī is the first night of the year—namely, the latter one; the former one is the last [night]."[8]

W.'s comment on the above is as follows: "All this, it seems, can only mean that, of two successive (nearly) full-moon nights in Phalgunī, the former, when the moon is nearer the former Phalgunī, is the last night of one year, and the other, the first night of the next year; and the only conclusion to be properly drawn from it is that the full-moon of the month Phālguna divides the two years."[9]

According to Whitney, the Indo-Aryans had not attained such astronomical exactitude as would enable them to draw a line between Pūrva and Uttara Phalgunī.

1 Vide paras 43-49

2 Vide paras 50-56

3 See para 46, and also *IA.*, 1895, p. 362

4 See para 52, and also *IA.*, 1895, p. 363

5-9 *IA.*, 1895, p. 363

W. believes that the statement has two parts, but he finds no reason why J. should take the two parts completely separately by an unaccountable procedure and infer from the one part that Phālguna was recognised by the *Brāhmaṇas* as the first month of the year, and from the other part that summer solstice was determined by the *Brāhmaṇas* to lie between the former and the latter Phalgunī's. He states that the sun in the Phalgunī's had no connection with the problem and that the *Brāhmaṇas* could not be supposed to possess such an astronomical exactitude as would enable them to draw a line between the former and latter Phalgunī's.[1] "What they [i.e., the *Brāhmaṇas*] have really done is bad and blundering enough, but quite of a piece with their general treatment of matters involving astronomical observation. For it is senseless to talk, in connection with the full-moon in Phālguna, of a year-limit between the two Phalgunī's; if the definition would fit the circumstances in a given year, it could not possibly do so in the year following, nor in the year after that, nor even in two years in succession."[2]. W. concedes that these *Brāhmaṇa* passages indicate one of the beginnings of the year in Phālguna, which may be due to various causes "besides the occurrence of the solstice near that group of stars 4000 B.C."[3]

Whitney admits that one of the year-beginnings may be in Phālguna, according to the *Brāhmaṇas*.

"With their customary looseness in regard to such matters, the ancient Hindus reckoned three, or five, or six, or seven seasons (ṛtu) in the year; and there was no controlling reason why any of these might not have been given the first place—the vacillating relations of the lunar months to the actual seasons adding their share of the confusion."[4] W. states that ancient four-month sacrifices are of primary importance, and that therefore all that was necessary was to arrange the year with any month as the first month for the convenience of the sacrifice.[5]

Other year-beginnings were also recognised for four-month sacrifices.

81. W. opposes J.'s assertion that "The later Vedic period has applied a correction consisting in the transfer of the initial point to Kṛittikā (the Pleiades); and this very circumstance gives their determination a real significance; it must have been nearly right at

1 *Ibid.*, pp. 363, 364
2-5 *Ibid.*, p. 364

the time of the correction."[1] W. finds want of candour on the part of J. for not adding a caveat to his former statement to the following effect: "provided the system of asterisms was really of Hindu origin and modification." W. states that the widely prevalent view among deep scholars, that Hindu asterismal system had no originality, specially as it is found in a large part of Asia, must have been known to J. The only question that remains to be solved by J. is "whether it was brought into India or carried out of India." Instead of doing that, "what possible grounds has Prof. Jacobi for regarding its Indian origin as so certain that the opposing view has no claim even to be referred to"? asks W.

Whitney thinks that the conception of vernal equinox at Kṛttikās is a borrowed one.

82. Some scholars, W. states, are of opinion that the source of knowledge of astronomy possessed by Indo-Aryans was China or Arabia. He himself as well as A. F. Weber looks upon Mesopotamia as the source. "Nothing in the *Rig-veda* nor in the *Brāhmaṇas*, and nothing in later Sanskrit literature, tends in any degree to give us the impression that the ancient Hindus were observers, recorders, and interpreters of astronomical phenomena. On the contrary, their treatment of such facts......shews the same looseness and heedlessness that is characteristic of Hindu genius everywhere in its relation to objective truth, to successive historical occurrences."[2] He finds that in the *Ṛgveda* there is no mention of the planets, and concludes from this omission that the Vedic poets were then not in a position to devise any asterismal system. It is true, he admits, that a late hymn or two of the *Ṛv.*, and passages in the *Brāhmaṇas*, show that the Vedic people knew of a year of 360 days, divided into 12 months of 30 days each,—which gave practically 354 solar days only. But "what their relation to one another, how their differences were reconciled, and by what method either reckoning was kept in unison with the true year, no one knows. The earliest so-called 'Vedic' astronomical manual the (Vedāṅga), the *Jyotisha*, whose first object, seemingly, it ought to be to give rules on such points, is mostly filled with unintelligible rubbish, and leaves us quite in the lurch as regards valuable information." A change came, and the Hindu astronomy was grounded on sound basis only when, the Greek

Whitney states that ignorance of astronomy in Ṛgvedic and later Vedic times is an admitted fact.

According to Whitney, it was in the first century A. D. that Indo-Aryans borrowed a true astronomical science from the Greeks.

1 *Ibid.*, p. 364

2 *Ibid.*, p. 365

influence came over it. And when. not long after the beginning of our era, the Hindus had borrowed from Greece a true astronomical science, the product of long-continued and accurate observation, they at once proceeded to cast it into an artificial form, founded on assumed and consciouly false data, adapting it to purely closet use, with exclusion of further observation : taking in as part of the data a grossly inaccurate determination of the positions of certain selected 'junction-stars' (*yogatārā*) of the asterisms, which positions they called 'dhruva' (fixed), thus virtually denying the precession. That such observers and reasoners as these should have been capable, some four or five thousand years before Christ, of determining, or believing themselves to have determined, the position of the summer solstice as between β and δ Leonis lacks to my mind any semblance of plausibility. Instead of shifting the beginning (mukha) of the asterismal series from Mṛigaśiras (Orion's head) to Kṛittikā (Pleiades) in the later Vedic period, I hold it as alone probable that they received the system from abroad with Kṛittikā at its head and would probably had retained it in that form until the present day but for the revolution wrought in their science by Greek teaching. When the beginning was shifted from Kṛittikā to Aśvinī (Aries), it was for good reason, and owing to the change of position of the equinox ; but the credit of this belongs to the Greeks, and not to the Hindus."[1]

(B) WHITNEY ON TILAK'S VIEWS

83. After the above review of J.'s position in regard to year-beginning, W. examines the relavant portion of T.'s *Orion* chapter by chapter. He accuses T. of attaching undue importance to Bhagavadgītā[2] which, due to its late date and secondary origin, would not be supported by western scholars. He praises T.'s excellent spirit of investigation, "with much and various learning" and "with commendable ingenuity", but all the same he thinks that T.'s arguments are in general "strained, its premises questionable, and the conclusions lacking in solidity."[3]

Whitney says that Tilak has not been able to prove his thesis that in 5th millennium B.C , the asterism Mṛgaśiras was close to vernal equinox.

1 *Ibid.*, p. 365

2 T. is said to have been led to his investigation by Śri Kṛṣṇa's claim in the Gītā that he was Mārgaśīrṣa among the months.

3 *IA.*, 1895, p. 365

According to W., one of the main objects in view in the *Orion* is the establishment of the fact that the asterism Mṛgaśiras (lit. 'deer's head') with its surroundings, or the constellation Orion with its neighbours, "was a great centre of observation and myth-making in the earliest time even back to the period of Indo-European or Aryan unity—and this, not only because of its conspicuous beauty as a constellation, but also, and principally, for its position close to the vernal equinox in the fifth millennium B.C."[1]

84. The second chapter of T.'s *Orion* is called "Sacrifice alias the Year." W. tries to refute T.'s contention in the following way:

Whitney opposes Tilak's theory that Sattra reflects the year,

"That there is a close relation between natural periods of time and the sacrifices is a matter of course; the morning and evening oblations depend upon the day; the new-moon and full-moon ceremonies, upon the natural month; the four-month or seasonal sacrifices, upon the recognised seasons; and so, when the round of the year had made itself plain, there were established rites to mark its recurrence. But Mr. Tilak appears to hold that the year was fixed and maintained by and for the sake of the great Sattra ('session') or protracted sacrifice that lasts a whole year."[2] W. thinks that T. wrongly views[3] "the year-sattra as a primitive Indo-European institution, the necessary auxiliary to a calendar", because he forgets that every ceremony of more than 12 days is called a *Sattra*, the *Sattras* being of a great variety of lengths, and because he cannot see that all of them "bespeak of a highly elaborated sacrificial system, implying orders of priests, accumulated wealth, and, one may even say, regulated city life."[4] He further points out "the utter and palpable mistake of T." in tracing in the *Ṛgveda* the two ayanas or halves of the year, "the northern and the southern—those, namely, in which the sun moves respectively northward and southward, from solstice to solstice, or else (for the word has both varieties of application) on the north and on the south of the equator from equinox to equinox",—in other words, *devayāna* and *pitṛyāna*,

1-2 *Ibid.*, p. 366

3 In support of his contention, W. quotes the following passage from *The Orion*, pp. 13, 14 : "Without a yearly *Sattra* regularly kept up, a Vedic Rishi could hardly have been able to ascertain and measure the time in the way he did .....The idea of a sacrifice extending over the whole year may be safely supposed to have originated in the old days of the history of the Aryan race."

4 *IA.*, 1895, p. 366

which according to W. have no such meaning. "There is, in fact, nothing yet brought to light in the *Rig-veda* to indicate, or even intimate, that in its time such things as *ayanas* and equinoxes and solstices, regarded as distances and points in the heavens, had ever been thought of; everything of the kind that the author of the *Orion* thinks to find there is projected into the oldest Veda out of the records of a much later period." According to W. "this fundamental error of T. is bad enough to vitiate his whole argument."[1]

Whitney finds that equinoxes and even solstices were unknown at the time of the *Ṛgveda*.

85. In dealing with the next chapter III of the *Orion*, on Kṛttikās, W. admits at once the main point of T. *viz.* that "in the earlier time the asterismal system began with Krittikā (Pleiades) instead of Aśvinī (Aries) which is conceded by every one."[2] His complaint is against T.'s bare mention (p. 6) of the crucial question of the origin of the system, though, according to W., he had no other alternative. For, "if he is in a position, as he claims, to prove that India had a yet earlier system beginning with Mrigaśiras (Orion), he has demonstrated the Hindu origin."[3] W. points out that a considerable part of the chapter is taken up in fully quoting, translating and discussing two parallel passages from the *Taittirīya* and *Kauṣītaki Brāhmaṇas*,[4] determining the different times of consecration [Dīkṣā] for the year-long Sattra, and concludes that the four different times are;

Whitney admits Tilak's main point that in earlier times the Indo-Aryan asterismal system began with Kṛttikās; but denies that Mṛgaśiras series was known to them.

(1) the last quarter in the month of Māgha (Ekāṣṭakā); (2) the full-moon of the following month Phālguna; (3) the full-moon of the next month Caitra, (4) four days before the full-moon (i.e. of Caitra: but some authorities regard Māgha as intended in the texts). W. states that T. rejects the above first two dates, because they are inconvenient due to cold and other causes and approves of the other two (actually one)[5].

The explanation regarding the four different times of consecration in the year-long Sattra as prescribed in the literatures.

1 *Ibid.*, p. 366

2-3 *Ibid.*, p. 367

4 This is a mistake. T. uses the *Taitt. Saṁ* and *Tāṇḍya Br.* for his purpose, and not *Taitt. Br.* and *Kāuṣ. Br.* For the omission of the *Kauṣ. Br.*, Th. criticises T. later on.

The required data for establishing the validity of Tilak's conclusion have not been supplied by him, says Whitney.

86. W. condemns T.'s dependence on the passages quoted from the *Taitt.-Saṃ.* and *Tāṇḍya-Br.*, by stating that "there is nothing to be fairly inferred from these quoted passages except that considerable diversity prevailed in practice, and was allowed, as regards time for commencing the Sattra and that the element of astronomical exactness did not enter into the case at all".[2] This conclusion of W. is based on his belief that T. was unable to establish three important data mentioned below. They, as W. says, would have been, if proved, valid premises for T.'s conclusion. The three data which require to be proved are :—

(1) "If, this Sattra were, as Mr. Tilak assumes, a counterpart of the year, established in primeval times on competent astronomical knowledge, for the purpose of keeping the calendar straight, and accordingly adapted precisely to the movements of the sun;

(2) "and if the *Vishuvant* or central day (with 180 days of ceremonies in a certain order preceding it, and 180 days of the same in a reverse order following it), were attached necessarily to an equinox, because the word *Vishuvant* implies an equal division of the day between light and darkness; and

(3) "if there were no way of explaining the series of alternative beginnings excepting by recognizing two of them as conservative traditions from times that fitted these astronomical conditions;—

then, and only then, we could use them as sufficient data, inferring from them the positions of the equinox, and hence, the epochs, at which they were successively established. But all these necessary conditions appear to be wanting......So far as any preference is shown in connection with the incidence of the *Vishuvant* day, it is for the solstice instead of the equinox, And the texts which set forth the different dates side by side are plainly unaware of any deeper reason for the choice of one instead of another."[2]

1 For the passages, see para 60.

2 *IA.*, 1895, p. 366

D. Thibaut's Arguments

(against Tilak and Jacobi)

Thibaut looks upon the views of Tilak and Jacobi to be identical, inasmuch as both of them prove the antiquity of the Vedas.

87. The aim of T.'s book *The Orion,* and J.'s article in the *IA.*, "On the Date of the Rigveda" is, according to Th., essentially one and the same; both of them attempt to prove from astronomical data contained in the *Vedas,* and *Brāhmaṇas* that these point to a time much more ancient than has been generally assumed.[1] Th. points out that difference between the two scholars is that while J. is bent on proving the antiquity of the civilization, T. is putting emphasis on the antiquity of the *Vedas* themselves.

For Th., the important point for decision is: whether the passages in question can be properly explained only on the hypothesis that they embody astronomical observations made by Vedic Aryans in the early times assumed by both writers.[2]

The two passages on the day on which Gavām-ayana sacrifice is to begin.

88. Th. takes up the two passages, which "contain various statements as to the day on which the introductory ceremony of consecration (*dīkṣhā*) for the so-called gavām-ayana sacrifice is to begin."[3] Not satisfied with others' renderings, Th. translates them himself. His translations are reproduced below.

Thibaut's translation of the passage from the *Taittirīya-Saṃhitā.*

Taitt. Saṃ., VII. 4. 8.—"Those who wish to consecrate themselves for a year (i.e., for the *gavām-ayana* which lasts a year) should consecrate themselves on (the day called) *ekāshṭakā.* For the *ekāshṭakā* is the wife of the year; in her he (i.e., the year) dwells that night. Manifestly beginning the year they (thus) consecrate themselves.—With a view to the injured (part) of the year consecrate themselves those who consecrate themselves on the *ekāshṭakā*; there are the two seasons whose name is 'end.' With a view to the reversed (*vyasta*) (part) of the year indeed consecrate themselves those who consecrate themselves on the *ekāshṭakā*; there are the two seasons whose name is 'end'.

"They should consecrate themselves on the Phalgunī full moon. The mouth of the year indeed is the Phalgunī full moon; beginning

1 *IA.*, 1895, p. 85

2 According to J., the period referred to in the Vedic literature ranges from about 4500 B.C. to about 2500 B.C., while according to T., it is from about 5000 B.C. to about 3000 B.C. (*Arctic Home*). *IA.*, 1895, *p. 85*

3 *Ibid.*, p. 88

the year from the mouth they consecrate themselves. In this there is one fault, *viz.*, that the *vishuvat*-day (the central day of the sacrifice) falls within the cloudy time. They should consecrate themselves on the Chitrā full moon. The mouth indeed of the year is the Chitrā full moon ; beginning the year from the mouth they consecrate themselves. In this there is not any fault.

"Four days before the full moon they should consecrate themselves ; for them the buying of the *soma* falls on the *ekāshṭakā* ; thereby they do not render the *ekāshṭakā* void. For them the pressing of the *soma* falls in the former (bright) half of the month. Their months are accomplished with a view to the former half. They rise (from the finished sacrifice) in the former half ; when they rise herbs and plants rise after them ; after them rises the fair fame. 'These sacrifices have prospered' ; after that all prosper."[1]

Thibaut's translation of the similar passage from the *Tāṇḍya-Brāhmaṇa.*

Tāṇḍya Brāhmaṇa V. 9.—"They should consecrate themselves on the *ekāshṭakā.* For the *ekāshṭakā* is the wife of the year ; in her he dwells that night. Manifestly beginning the year they consecrate themselves. In this there is that fault that non-rejoicing they step down into the water. With a view to the cleft (*vichchhinna*) (part) of the year they consecrate themselves who consecrate themselves on the *ekāshṭakā* ; there are the two seasons whose name is 'end'. With a view to the injured (part) of the year they consecrate themselves who consecrate themselves with a view to the seasons called 'end'. Therefore the consecration is not to be performed on the *ekāshṭakā.*

"They should consecrate themselves in Phālguna. The mouth of the year indeed is the Phālgunī (full moon) ; beginning the year from the mouth they consecrate themselves.—In this there is the fault that the *Vishuvat*-day falls within the cloudy time. They should consecrate themselves on the Chitrā full moon. The eye indeed of the year is the Chitrā full moon ; on the side of the face is the eye ; from the face (i.e., beginning) commencing the year they consecrate themselves. In this there is no fault.—They should consecrate themselves four days before full moon. For them the buying of the *soma* falls on the *Vishuvat*, etc. etc. (without any essential divergence from the concluding portion of the *Taittirīya* passage)."[2]

1 *IA.*, 1895, pp. 85, 86

2 *Ibid.*, p. 86

89. Th. then makes a general remark as follows: "As the *gavām-ayana* is a festival celebration extending over a whole year, it is antecedently probable that it, or its introductory ceremony, should begin on some day which marked the beginning of the year, and that, therefore, the four different terms referred to in the passages above translated should represent either different beginnings of the year which were in use at one and the same time, or else, possibly, beginnings acknowledged at different periods."[1] Th. states that J. and T. adopt the latter view, and that T. assumes with the *Mīmāṃsakas* that the last term, *viz.*, 'four days before the full moon' refers to the full moon of the month Māgha.

Gavām-ayana may coincide with year-beginning (Thibaut).

The *Taitt.-Saṃ.* and *Tāṇḍya-Br.* thus finally decide in favour of a beginning of the sacrificial year nearly coinciding with the civil beginning of the year. He further puts the whole case for T. in the following words: "It is probable that the civil year began on the day of the winter solstice, and we therefore may conclude that the two Vedic books, which decide in favour of the *gavām-ayana* beginning on or about the full moon of Māgha, were composed in the period when the summer solstice was in the asterism Maghās. This agrees with the position which the *Veda*[2] assigns to Kṛittikās as the first of the Nakshatras; which position has always been explained as pointing back to the time when the vernal equinox was in Kṛittikās. Now Kṛittikās marked the vernal equinox, and Maghās the summer solstice, at about 2350 B.C., and this, therefore, is the time at which we must suppose the *Taittirīya-Saṃhitā* and similar works to have been composed. If then, we further find that the *Taittirīya Saṃhitā* mentions two other terms for the beginning of the year-sacrifice, *viz.*, the full moon in Phalgunī and Chitrā, we must conclude from analogy that those two terms also once marked the winter solstice; and the rules prescribing them thus lead us back to about 4000 and 6000 B.C.[3] respectively. Those rules were remembered at the time when the *Taittirīya Saṃhitā* was composed, but, as no longer agreeing with the actual state of things, were mentioned only to be set aside in favour of the rule then in accordance with reality, *viz.*, the one which makes the winter solstice coincide with full moon in Maghās."[4]

Thibaut explains how Tilak arrives at the year 4000 B.C.

1 *Ibid.*, p. 86
2 *Ibid.*, p. 86
3 According to Tilak's *Orion*
4 *IA.*, 1895, pp. 86, 87

90. The statement by Th. quoted above gives a gist of the views of T. as found in the *Orion*. According to Th., J. supports the rule fixing the beginning of the year-sacrifice on the full moon in Phalgunī, which rule as J. says was prevalent from the time when the winter (sic) solstice occurred along with the full moon in Phalgunī, i.e., about 4500 B.C., in agreement with other Vedic passages making the summer solstice fall along with Phalgunī. Th. states that J. takes the last term (4 days before the full moon) to be connected with Citrā (Caitra) fullmoon and thinks it to be a later addition.[1]

The beginning of the year-long sacrifice in Phalgunī full moon about 4500 B.C. is supported by Jacobi.

91. Th. feels that he has no right to declare the conclusions arrived at by J. and T. alike to be altogether imposible. "Vedic civilization and literature *may* be considerably older than has hitherto been supposed, and reminiscences of ancient observations *may* have been preserved in books themselves belonging to a much later period".[2] But before Th. accepts the conclusions of J. and T., he wants to be convinced that the passages on which the conclusions are based, admit of no other interpretation than that put on them.

Before accepting the findings of Jacobi and Tilak, Thibaut wants to be convinced that the passages quoted admit of no other interpretation than that given by them.

"Are we really obliged, we must ask ourselves, to ascend with Jacobi and Tilak to 4000 B.C., and to follow the latter scholar even into the dim distance of 6000 B.C., or else to precipitate ourselves, with Jacobi, in the opposite direction as far down as 200 B.C.? Or is there, perhaps, after all, some means of reconciling the different statements as to the beginning of the *gavām-ayana* in such a way as to make them fit in with one and the same period, and that a period not too widely remote from the time to which works such as the *Taittirīya Saṃhitā* and *Tāṇḍya Brāhmaṇa* have hitherto been ascribed?" Th. endeavours to show that this can be accomplished and that conclusions arrived at by J. and T. cannot be upheld.[3]

Thibaut thinks that there is a *via media*, and conclusions of Jacobi and Tilak need not be accepted *in toto*.

92. Th. then discusses a passage from the *Kauṣītaki-Brāhmaṇa* (XIX. 2. 3). He complains that T. has not discussed it,

1 *Ibid.*, p. 87 2 *Ibid.*, p. 87 3 *Ibid.*, p. 87

The *Kauṣītaki* passage.

because, as Th. thinks, T. would have arrived at a different conclusion if he had taken sufficient notice of the *Kaus.* passage. We reproduce below the text in question which was omitted by Th., only its translation being given by him.

ते पुरस्तादेव दीक्षाप्रसवान् कल्पयन्ते तैषस्यामावास्याया एकाह उपरिष्टाद्दीक्षेरन् माघस्य वेत्याहुस्तदुभयं व्युदितं तैषस्य त्वेवोदिततरमिव त एतं त्रयोदशमधिचरं मासमाप्नुवन्त्येतावान्वै संवत्सरो यदेष त्रयोदशो मास स्तत्रैव सर्वः संवत्सर आप्तो भवति ॥२॥

स वै माघस्यामावास्यायामुपवसत्युदङ्ङावत्स्यर्न्नुपेमेवसन्ति प्रायणीयेनातिरात्रेण यक्ष्यमाणास्तदेनं प्रथममाप्नुवन्ति तं चतुर्विंशेनाऽऽरभन्ते तदारम्भणीयस्याऽऽरम्भनीयत्वं स षण्मासानुदङ्ङेति तमूर्ध्वैः षडहैरनुयन्ति स षण्मासानुदङ्ङित्वा तिष्ठते दक्षिणाऽऽवर्तत्स्यन्नुपेमे वसन्ति वैषुवतीयेनाह्ना यक्ष्यमाणास्तदेनं द्वितीयामाप्नुवन्ति स षण्मासान् दक्षिणैति तमावृत्तैः षडहैरनुयन्ति स षण्मासान् दक्षिणेत्वातिष्ठत उदङावत्स्यैन्नुपेमे वसन्ति महाव्रतीयेनाह्ना यक्ष्यमाणास्तदेनं तृतीयमाप्नुवन्ति तं यत् त्रिराप्नुवन्ति त्रेधा विहितो वै संवत्सरः संवत्सरस्यैवाऽऽप्त्यै तदुतैषाऽपि गीयते। अहोरात्राणि विदधदूर्णा वा इव धीर्यः षन्मासो दक्षिणा नित्यः षड्उदङ्ङेति सूर्य इति षड्ढ्येष उदङ्मासानेति षड्दक्षिणा तद्वै न तस्मिन् काले दीक्षेरन्ननागतं सस्यं भवति दहरकान्यहानि भवन्ति संवेषमाना अवभृथादुदायन्ति तस्मादत्र न दीक्षेरंश्चैत्रस्यामावस्याया एकाह उपरिष्टाद्दीक्षेरन्ननागतं सस्यं भवति महान्यहानि भवन्त्यसंवेषमाना अवभृथादुदायन्ति तस्मादेतत् स्थितम् ॥३॥

"They are to consecrate themselves one day before[1] the new moon of Taisha[2], or of Māgha: thus they say. Both these

Translation of the text by Thibaut.

(alternatives) are discussed; that of Taisha, however, is more agreed to, as it were.[3] They (thus) obtain the additional thirteenth month. So great indeed is the year as that thirteenth month; then the whole year is obtained. He (the sun) indeed rests on the new moon

1 It should be 'after'—evidently a printing mistake.

2 Taisha=Pauṣa

3 "Both of these views are current but that as to Taisha is the more current as it were." —Keith, the *Rigvedic Brāhmṇas*, (Tr.), p. 452 [Tr. of passage from the *Kauṣ.-Br.*]

day of Māgha, being about to turn towards the north.[1] Thus they rest who are about to perform the rites of the *prāyaṇīya atirātra* (the first day on which *soma* is pressed). Thus they reach him [the sun] for the first time....He goes for six months towards the north[2] ; they follow him with the ascending celebrations of six days each. He having gone six months towards the north[3] stands still, being about to turn towards the south.[4] Thus they stop, being about to perform the rites of the *Vaishuvatīya* day. Thus they reach him for the second time. He goes six months towards the south.[5] They follow him with the returning celebrations of six days each. Having gone six months towards the south[6] he stands still being about to turn towards the north.[7] Thus they stop, being about to perform the rites of the *Mahāvratīya* day. Thus they reach him for the third time. Because they reach him three times, the year is arranged threefold ; for obtaining the year (they do thus). About this there is sung a sacrificial stanza 'Arranging the days and nights like a wise spider ; six months always towards the south and six towards the north wanders the sun'.[8] For he goes six months towards the north, six towards the south.[9]

"They are not to consecrate themselves at that time. The grass has not yet come out, the days are short ; shivering they come out of the *avabhṛitha*-bath. Therefore, they are not to consecrate

1 Keith translates the word as "northwards" and I think more properly. According to T., Uttarāyaṇa is susceptible of two interpretations, viz. (1) "turning towards the north from the southern-most point", (2) the passage of the sun into the northern hemisphere, i.e., to the north of the equator. If we adopt the first meaning, the Uttarāyaṇa and the year must be held to commence from the winter solstice, while if the second interpretation be correct, the Uttarāyaṇa and the year must have once commenced with the vernal equinox ; .....the second of the two interpretations, given above, is more likely to be the older one. (Tilak, *The Orion*, p. 26). Keith's translation supports the second interpretation and Th.'s translation supports the first.

2 'He goes north for six months.' —Keith

3 'Having gone north for six months.' —Keith

4 'Being about to turn southwards.'—Keith

5 'He goes south for six months.' —Keith

6 'Having gone south for six months.' Keith

7 'Being about to turn north.' —Keith

8 'With regard to this this sacrificial verse is sung:
Obtaining the days and nights,
Like a cunning spider,
For six months south constantly,
For six north the sun goeth'—Keith

9 'For six months he goes north, six south'. —Keith

themselves then. They are to consecrate themselves one day after the new moon of Chaitra. The corn has come out then ; the days are long ; without shivering they come out of the *avabhṛitha*-bath. Therefore this is the established rule."[1]

Three different terms for beginning Gavāmayana are found by Thibaut.

From the above passage of the *Kauṣītaki-Brāhmaṇa,* Th. finds three different terms for the beginning of the Gavāmayana:

(1) the day following the new moon of Taiṣa ;

(2) the day following the new moon of Māgha ;

(3) the day following the new moon of Caitra.[2]

Thibaut reduces the year-beginnings to two dates,—Taiṣa, and Caitra.

93. Th. thinks that the second term is a variation of the first. Hence he confines his attention to "that term which the [said] *Brāhmaṇa* declares to be preferable, i.e., the beginning of the *dīkshā* on the day following on the new moon of Taisha."[3] Further, by new moon, Th. understands, following Vināyaka's commentary on the *Kauṣ-Br.*, the new moon preceding the full moon of the particular month. He thinks, however, that this does not compel him to assume with Vināyaka that a month is reckoned from full moon to full moon so that the months would begin with the dark half (although to this also there would be no particular objection).[4]

The interpretation of new moon by Thibaut.

He finds no reason for strictness of terminology for the time of the *Kauṣītaki-Brāhmaṇa.*

94. "In the strict terminology of later times", continues Th., "indeed the *amāvasyā* of Taisha could be the *amāvasyā* preceding the full moon in Tishya, only if the month Taisha were reckoned from full moon in Mṛigaśiras to full moon in Tishya ; while if it were reckoned from new moon to new moon, the *amāvasyā* of Taisha would mean the last *tithi* of the dark half following on full moon in Tishya and preceding full moon in Maghās. But there is no reason compelling us to assume such strictness of terminology for the time of the *Brāhmaṇa,* especially when we consider that new moon is, strictly speaking, not a lunar day, but only the moment when the dark half comes to an end and the light half begins ; so that the beginning of the first day of the

1 *IA.*, 1895, pp. 87, 88

2 The subject has been gone into a later para.

3 *Ibid.*, p. 88

4 *Ibid.*, p. 88

light half has as much right to be called '*amāvasyā*' as the end of the last day of the dark half."[1]

95. According to Th., as the Dīkṣā begins one day after the new moon which precedes full moon in Tiṣya, celebration of *upavasatha* "which immediately precedes the first day on which Soma is pressed, falls on the new month of Māgha (i.e., the new moon preceding full moon in Maghās)".[2] He thinks this to be accurate, for from the day after Taiṣa new moon up to Māgha new moon there elapse 29 days, 17 of which go for Dīkṣā, and 12 for Upasad. "The result of this arrangement is that the real celebration, as distinguished from all introductory ceremonies, begins together with the 'resting of the sun' before he starts on his progress towards the north. The text thus clearly indicates that what is to be aimed at is the coincidence of the beginning of the year-sacrifice with the winter solstice".[3]

Thibaut shows how the beginning of year-long sacrifice coincides with winter solstice.

96. The reason for preference of the next day to the new moon in Caitra, is that the season is more advanced and agreeable, the days are longer, and the water more pleasant for bathing.

Why Citrā new moon is preferred.

97. In explaining the divergences in the year-beginning, Th. states that "The impression which the coupling of the two alternative beginnings thus leaves in our mind is that the original intention and practice of the Kaushītakins was to begin their year-sacrifice on the day of the winter solstice, thus following the sun in its upward course with the first six sacrificial months and again in its downward course with the latter six months. But gradually the sacrifice, as it happens in such cases, became more and more formal; the old beginning was no longer insisted upon, and a new one, more convenient in several respects, was substituted. But there is nothing to indicate that the two beginnings allowed are connected with beginnings of the civil year, recognised at different periods. Some sacrificers preferred the solstitial beginning, some the vernal one; that is all".[4]

The older practice of beginning yearly sacrifice on winter solstice was not kept up and a more convenient beginning was adopted, Thibaut states.

98. Th. points out that the *Kauṣ.* passage has another

1 *Ibid.*, p. 88
2 *Ibid.*, p. 88
3 *Ibid.*, p. 88
4 *Ibid.*, p. 89

The *Kauṣītaki-Br.* states that the winter-solstice coincides with the new moon of Māgha, i.e., it occurs at the beginning of the white half of Māgha according to Thibaut.

importance, *viz.*, that it contains a definite statement regarding the relation of the lunar calendar of the time to the solar year. "It says that the winter-solstice coincides with the new moon of Māgha, i.e., with the new moon preceding full moon in Maghās."[1] Th. finds here well-known ground, for a well-known doctrine of the *Jyotiṣa Vedāṅga* is that the winter solstice takes place at the beginning of the white half of Māgha (or the end of the *amāvasyā* of Pauṣa).[2]

The *Kauṣītaki-Br.* belongs to a period when the winter solstice was in Śraviṣṭhā —not an ancient date. from which the dates of the *Taittirīya-Saṃhitā* and *Tāṇḍya-Brāhmaṇa* are not distant, states Thibaut.

99. All these facts lead Th. to conclude that the winter solstice itself is in *Śraviṣṭhās*, etc., etc.: in fact, from this the whole system of *Jyotiṣa Vedāṅga* follows[3] we must finally conclude that the *Kauṣītaki-Brāhmaṇa*, "unless it be assumed to record observations made at an earlier time, belongs to the period when the winter-solstice was supposed to be in Śravishṭhās".[4] In plain words, "the data which the *Kaushītaki-Brāhmaṇa* supplies concerning the beginning of the gavām-ayana do in no way lead us back into very ancient time".[5] Th. then poses before himself the question, whether it is possible to interpret the *Taittirīya* and *Tāṇḍya* texts in a somewhat analogous way, and thus "connect them with one and the same period, not very distant from the period of the *Kaushītaki-Brāhmaṇa*". He goes on to enquire, if the alternative dates for Dīkṣā given by the *Taitt.-Saṃ* and *Tāṇḍya-Br.* can be accounted for by the assumption that at one and the same time the *gavām-ayana* was optionally begun at different periods of the year, for reasons sufficiently valid to explain such differences, He finds the answer to be in the affirmative.[6]

The expression, 'Phalgunī full moon is the mouth of the year', is being examined by Thibaut.

100. Th. then examines the meaning of the passage that the full moon in Phalgunī is the mouth, i.e., beginning of the year. Th. says that "This statement, or the closely related one that 'the (month) Phālguna is the mouth of the year' occurs in numerous other places of the *Brāhmaṇas*, and must therefore be held to represent an opinion generally prevailing in what we may call the *Brāhmaṇa*-period. Where then has this beginning of the year to be placed? Either, we feel naturally

1 *Ibid.*, p. 89 2 *Ibid.*, p. 89. 1100 B.C. according to Thibaut.
3 *IA.*, 1895, p. 89 4 *Ibid.*, p. 89 5 *Ibid.*, p. 89 6 *Ibid.*, p. 89

inclined to reply, at one of the solstices or at one of the equinoxes.

Thibaut states that the Phalgunī full moon did not coincide with vernal equinox in the Brāhmaṇa-period.

Now that the solstices were, in India, looked upon as marking the beginning of the year we know positively from the *Jyotish Vedāṅga* and similar works (not to speak of the whole later literature), and also from the *Kauṣhītaki* passage discussed above; implies the view that the year-sacrifice is made to begin with the winter solstice for the winter solstice is viewed as the beginning of the natural or civil year. Moreover, the *Vedas* contain numerous references to the northern and southern progress of the sun, it, therefore, is antecedently probable that the solstices should have formed starting points for the civil year.[1] According to Th., the view of T. and J. that the Phalgunī full-moon once marked for the Indians the winter solstice is not unlikely. He disbelieves, however, that "the passages about the *gavām-ayana* in the two *Brāhmaṇas* should contain an agglomerate of rules that had originated at periods widely remote from each other, and we, moreover, have the direct statement of the Kaushītakins that the winter solstice happens on new moon preceding full moon in Maghās ; we, therefore, may at any rate, attempt to account on other grounds for the statement that Phalgunī-full moon is the beginning of the year. Now, it is, of course, at once clear that, in the *Brāhmaṇa* period, full moon in Phalgunī could not have coincided with the vernal equinox."[2] Immediately after this, Th. gives a general advice thus: "We, moreover, must, apart from this particular case, disabuse our minds of the notion of the

Thibaut wants that the notion that Indo-Aryans knew of equinoxes should be given up.

equinoxes—vernal or autumnal—having been of any importance for the Hindus previous to the time when the influence of the Greek astronomy began to make itself felt."[3] The reason for this, as given by Th., is that the equinoxes naturally do not attract attention in the same way as the solstices do ; for at

1 *Ibid.*, p. 89

2 *Ibid.*, pp. 89, 90. Cf. Tilak, *The Orion*, p. 26: "The old order of seasons given in the passage above quoted (*Śata-Br.*, II. 1, 3, 1-3) however clearly states that Vasanta in old days commenced with vernal equinox. We can now understand why Vasanta has been spoken of as the first season. "The passage runs as follows : वसन्तो ग्रीष्मो वर्षाः । ते देवा ऋतवः शरद्धेमन्तः शिशिरस्ते पितरो य एवा पूर्यतेऽर्धमासः स देवा योऽपक्षीयते स पितरोऽहरेव देवा रात्रिः पितरः पुनरह्नः पूर्वाह्णो देवा अपराह्णः पितरः ।

2 *Ibid.*, p. 90 3 *Ibid.*, p. 90

the equinoxes, the motion of the sun—be it northwards or southwards—undergoes no noticeable change, equal length of day and night being not easily detected. Th. states that the patent characteristics of solstices viz. their greatest deviations from normal state, when the sun stands highest or lowest, the days become longest or shortest, the shadows shortest or longest, and the sun turns north or south, attract attention easily. Another more important point, according to Th., is that in India, the vernal equinox at any rate does not in any way mark the revolution of the seasons. "It is in agreement with all this that the equinoxes or anything connected with them are nowhere in Vedic literature referred to, either directly or indirectly."[1] Th. then warns that if no immediate and obvious connection with solstice is found in the reference to the beginning of the year in Vedic literature, "there is no valid reason for thinking alternately of equinoxes in regard to year-beginning; other likely points from which the year might have commenced must be looked out."[2]

Thibaut thinks that Cāturmāsya-sacrifice offers an explanation of year-beginning.

101. According to Th., the *Cāturmāsya*-sacrifice presupposes the subdivision of the year into three seasons, This may offer an explanation of year-beginning. He disagrees with J. when the latter opposes the view that "the beginning of the oldest Indian years coincided with the beginnings of those four-monthly periods rather than with the equinoxes."[3] Th. concedes that so far as the beginning of the year, made in the beginning of the rainy season, the most defined period, is concerned, the time-table of J. may be correct ; but Th. is of opinion that J.'s remarks are wrong in actual allotment of the months to the three seasons. A division which, on the basis of three different seasons,[4] distinguishes three four-monthly periods can never be quite accurate, because the rainy season occupies less than four months, strictly speaking a little more than three months.[5] But as a four-monthly division is to be adhered to, Th. thinks a compromise becomes necessary, and in that case, the four months for the rainy season would be June to September, or better,—end of first

According to Thibaut the 3 four-monthly divisions are :
1. June—Oct.
2. Oct.—Feb.
3. Feb.—June.

1 *Ibid.*, p. 90 2 *Ibid.*, p. 90 3 *Ibid.*, p. 90

4 Th. in a footnote states that the Indian year broadly divides itself into seasons consecutively—warm, rainy and cold ; in course of time two more seasons were added—spring before warm and autumn before cold. The system of six seasons is an artificial one. —*IA.*, 1895, p. 90 fn.

5 *Ibid.*, 1895, pp. 90, 91

week, or first third, of June to end of first week, or first third, of October.[1]—not from July to October nor from summer solstice to 20th October. So the two other seasons would be according to Th.: (1) from the earlier part of February (the increase of warmth being perceptible due to advent of summer) to the earlier part of June,—warm season ; and (2) from the earlier part of October to the earlier part of February (a refreshing coolness being felt in early October[2]),—cold season.

The corresponding sacrifices for the three divisions of the year.

102. Th. then examines what the *Brāhmaṇas* state in connection with the *Cāturmāsya.* He points out that the *Śatapatha-Brāhmaṇa* refers to sacrifices called *Cāturmāsya* which mark the beginning of the seasons (Ṛtumukhāni), and that they are as follows:

1. Vaiśvadeva—to be performed on the Phalgunī or the Citrā Paurṇamāsī (full moon) ;
2. Varuṇapraghāsās—to be performed on the Āṣāḍhī or the Śrāvaṇī full moon;
3. Sākamedhas—to be performed on the Kārttikī or Āgrahāyaṇī full moon.

In the description of Cāturmāsya, Vaiśvadeva is always mentioned first, so Thibaut thinks the year-beginning in Brāhmaṇa-period must have been in warm season.

Th. states that the texts always mention Vaiśvadeva first. From this he concludes that in the *Brāhmaṇa*-period the prevailing opinion was that "the year begins with the warm season."[3]

103. Th. then states that the *Kaus.-Br.* informs of the position of Phalgunī full moon in relation to solstice. According to the *Kauṣ.*-

1 From 7th or 10th June to 7th or 10th October

2 *IA.*, 1895, p. 91. This may be arranged as follows:

Varṣā	June to October
Śita	October to February
Grīṣma	February to June

3 *IA.*, 1895, p. 91

By reference to the *Kauṣītaki-Brāhmaṇa,* Thibaut finds that Phalgunī full moon, taking place 1½ months after winter solstice, is the warm season and the beginning of the 4-monthly divisions, and therefore the mouth of the year.

Br., "the winter solstice coincides with new moon preceding the Māghī full moon. Full moon in Phalgunī thus takes place one and a half month after the winter solstice, i.e., about the end of the first week in February, and this, as we have seen, is a period which may not unusually be looked upon as the beginning of the warm season. We now fully understand why the Phalgunī-full moon is called the mouth of the year; it marks the beginning of that four-monthly division of the year, which is generally considered the first one. And we further observe the full agreement between the statements about the Phalgunī-full-moon, and what the texts say in so many places about spring being the first season, the mouth of the seasons. For spring constitutes the former half of the four-monthly warm season. The beginning of the spring of the *Brāhmaṇas* is thus in no way connected with the vernal equinox, but rather takes place one and half months before it."[1]

Thibaut examines the different dates of year-beginning as given in the *Taitt.-Saṃ.* and *Taṇḍya-Br.*

104. The above are the preliminary remarks of Th. If the rules given by *Taitt,-Saṃ.* and *Tāṇḍya-Br.* about the beginning of the *gavām-ayana* are judged, by keeping the above conclusions in view, they become clear and coherent, states Th. He examines the different dates for beginning the year. He justifies the rejection of the beginning on the *ekāṣṭakā* day (the 8th day after full moon in Māgha) on the ground of its falling within the season which is the 'end' of the year (last month before the Phalgunī full-moon which marks the beginning of the year), and on the ground that the water is then unpleasantly cold for bathing (*Tāṇḍya.-Br.*).[2] The mention of Phālgunī full moon as the proper day for beginning the sacrifice, because it is the mouth of the year, is in proper order, according to Th. He justifies the rejection of this day also on the ground that the Viṣuvat then falls within the cloudy season, Th. states that if the *dīkṣā* takes place on the 7th February, the *Viṣuvat* falls at the end of August, which is within

1 *Ibid.,* p. 91

2 Th. does not admit J.'s contention that those sacrificing on the Phalgunī-fullmoon (i.e., 24 days after ekāṣṭakā) sacrifice when the water does not become sensibly warmer. On the other hand, he thinks that the difference would be a perceptible one ; and that the question loses its importance as the Phalgunī-fullmoon is rejected immediately afterwards. —*IA.,* 1895, p. 92

the rainy season; and that those who sacrifice on the day of Caitrī-full moon are justified, because the *Viṣuvat* falls at the end of September, when rains are over.[1]

105. According to Th., the reasons for mentioning Phālgunī and Caitrī-fullmoons, as alternate beginning of *gavām-ayana* on the one hand, and for the different periods for the Cāturmāsya sacrifices on the other, are the same. He states that the *Brāhmaṇas* and some *Sūtras* prescribe Phālgunī, Āṣāḍhī and Kārttikī fullmoons (strict beginnings of 3 fundamental seasons) ; and that some other Sūtras give the times as Caitrī, Śrāvaṇī and Āgrahāyaṇī fullmoons (i.e. not the beginnings, but earlier parts of the seasons). Th. reminds us that as lunar months lag behind the seasons, the Phālgunī full moon occurring on the 7th February in one year, will fall 12 days earlier next year, and 24 days earlier in the third year, so that by that time it will be 24 days less remote from the winter solstice than at first. This will not go on for ever. For, taking the cue from the *Jyotiṣa Vedāṅga*, Th. thinks that the disturbed harmony between the lunar and solar year would be restored by intercalation of a month in the middle of the third year. The Vaiśvadeva sacrificer, mentioned above, (para 102), may like to begin in the spring and therefore on Caitrī Paurṇamāsī which is considered to be proper by Th. instead of Phālgunī.[2]

Thibaut adduces his reasons for mentioning Phālgunī and Caitrī full moons as alternative beginnings.

Thibaut on intercalation.

106. To complete the discussion of the two passages from the *Taitt.-Saṃ* and the *Tāṇḍya.-Br.*, Th. takes up the words 'Ekāṣṭakā' and '4 days before full moon' found at the beginning and at the end of the passages. "The ekāṣhṭakā the commentators declare to be the eighth day of the dark half of Māgha, i.e., the eighth day after full moon in Maghās, the months being counted as beginning with the light half." Th. states that according to J., those who wished to perform all Introductory Rites before the Phālgunī-fullmoon day advocated this meaning of the word ekāṣṭakā, *viz.*, 8th day of the dark half of Māgha, in order that the real sacrifice might commence at the true beginning of the year. It is pointed out by Th. that J. himself

Ekāṣṭakā is connected with beginning on the amāvasyā of Taiṣa or Māgha, according to Thibaut.

1 *IA.*, 1895, p. 92

2 According to some authorities, the Vaiśvadeva sacrifice might be offered on Vaiśākhī-fullmoon.—*IA.*, 1895, p. 92

allots 24 days for these Introductory Rites, but the time from 8th of the dark half of Māgha to Phālgunī-fullmoon comprises only 22 days (and not 24). According to Th., the reference to ekāṣṭakā as the 'wife of the year' in several places of the texts, and the mention of some special rites in connection with ekāṣṭakā emphasise the importance of the same. Ekāṣṭakā "was, in fact, specially connected with the beginning of the new, or end of the old, year. If the year is viewed as beginning with Phalgunī-fullmoon, the light half of Phālguna, although really preceding the new year, might yet be viewed to belong to the new year, just because it is the light waxing half of the month, and in that case the *ekāshṭakā*, as marking the last quarter of the last waning half of the old year might not inappropriately be viewed as representing the end of the old year. It might, in fact, be viewed so also, if the months are reckoned from full moon to full moon, in which case the whole of Phālguna, i.e., the month preceding Phalgunī-fullmoon, would belong to the old year."[1] In this connection, Th. mentions another possibility. He states that if the months are counted from full moon to full moon then the dark half of Māgha is the half that follows the Pauṣi-fullmoon, and that the 8th day of the dark half of Māgha would in that case precede the solstice which occurs (as in the *Kauṣ.-Br.* and the *Vedāṅga-Jyotiṣa*) on the new moon day preceding Māghī-fullmoon. "The *ekāṣhṭakā* would then be the last quarter [of the month] preceding the winter solstice, and as such represent the end of that form of the year, which is reckoned from winter solstice to winter solstice." From the aforesaid remarks it becomes clear that the line of thinking of Th. appears to be that the *Taitt.-Saṃ.* and the *Tāṇḍya-Br.* mean by saying that the *gavām-ayana* begins on the ekāṣṭakā that the sacrifice should commence on the amāvasyā of Taiṣa (Pauṣa) or Māgha—both the beginnings being connected with the winter solstice. Th. notes that his last explanation goes against the Sūtra-writers who are in favour of taking ekāṣṭakā as the 8th day after Māghī-fullmoon.[2]

Th. states that the above explanation makes the objection to sacrifices on ekāṣṭakā day intelligible ; ekāṣṭakā falls within the last season of the year,—this season may precede Phalgunī-full-

1 *IA.*, 1895, p. 93 2 *Ibid.*, p. 93

Th. points out that this explanation is contradicted by those Sūtra Texts which define ekāṣṭakā as the 8th of the dark half of Māgha after Māghī-full-moon.

moon or winter solstice (अन्तनामानावृत्तू) ; it is cold season, therefore *ārtta* or distressed, injured ; Vyasta or Vicchinna refers, according to the commentators, to turning of the year in winter solstice.[1]

The meaning of '4 days before the full moon' is, according to Thibaut, 4 days before the full moon of Caitra.

107. In regard to the meaning of 4 days before the full moon, Th. does not think it to be an item of much importance. "If we, with the *Mīmāmsakas*, decide for the Māghī-full-moon, we have a beginning of the year in the same month as the *ekāshṭakā* (or at any rate separated from the latter by twelve days only) ; if, on the other hand, we decide for Chaitrī-fullmoon, the term nearly coincides with the third term,"[1] Th.'s opinion is therefore in favour of Caitrī-fullmoon. He says that he has the highest regard for the Mīmāmsakas, but in this case he is unable to accept their view. As this expression '4 days before the full moon', is immediately after the word 'Caitrī-fullmoon', he connects one with the other, and the ekāṣṭakā mentioned thereafter he takes to be the ekāṣṭakā following Caitrī-fullmoon.[2]

Gavām-ayana began in winter solstice, states Thibaut.

Th. thinks that he has shown that "The *Taittirīya* and *Tāṇḍya* passages about the beginning terms [periods] of gavām-ayana can be explained quite satisfactorily and coherently, if viewed as referring to the time when the winter solstice had the position assigned to it in the *Kaushītaki Brāhmaṇa* and *Jyotisha Vedāṅga*."[3]

Thibaut states that equinoxes were not mentioned in Vedic literature.

108. After a criticism of the view that *Rv.*, VII. 103 [Frog song] and Sūtras bearing on Upākaraṇa refer to year-beginning, Th. emphasises his previous remark that "in Vedic literature, the equinoxes are never mentioned, and hence in our chronological speculations we are not warranted in referring to them as probable starting points of the Vedic year."[4] He then examines the statements of J. and T. that Kṛttikās head an old list of Nakṣatras. This fact implies a recognition of the vernal equinox once lying in Kṛttikās. Th. however has never been able to find anything like a valid reason for this sort of conclusion. It is however found to have been

1 *Ibid.*, p. 93
2 *Ibid.*, pp. 93, 94
3 *Ibid.*, p. 94
4 *Ibid.*, p. 96

Thibaut states that year-beginning with the vernal equinox became prevalent among the Indo-Aryans through Greek influence.

universally used as the head of a series of Nakṣatras in the Vedic texts, Th. explains this by saying that it was the involuntary projection of the conception of the later Nakṣatra series with Aśvinī at its head, into the past. Th. states that when the system of Indian astronomy was cast into modern shape, the Indo-Aryans noticing appearance of Aśvinī as the background of the vernal equinox, in imitation, repeated it in connection with Kṛttikā as the background of the vernal equinox. The recognition of the importance attached to year-beginning with the vernal equinox, according to Th., was entirely due to Greek influence. Th. claims that he has already shown that, in the *Brāhmaṇa* period, equinoxes did not come into consideration at all in connection with seasons,—the spring falling midway between the winter solstice and vernal equinox.[1]

Thibaut thinks that equinoxes did not come into consideration at all in the *Brāhmaṇa* period.

109. Th. then considers T.'s argument (in Ch. II of the *Orion*) that distinct traces of the oldest year-beginning with vernal equinox are to be found in the term Viṣuvat which means originally 'the day when the night and day are equal', so that the central Viṣuvat day of the year-sacrifices like Gavām-ayana, etc. "must have been one of the equinoxes, and hence the sacrifice must have begun at the other equinox: whence we may conclude that equinox was viewed as the beginning of the year."[2] Th. finds no authority for taking the Viṣuvat in the sense taken by T. According to Th., the Viṣuvat means 'that which belongs to both sides equally', 'that which occupies the middle,' implying that the Viṣuvat day is the central day of the sacrifice, wherever that day may fall. Originally the Viṣuvat was meant to coincide with the summer solstice (June-July). When the beginning of the sacrifice had been moved to the beginning of spring, the Viṣuvat (central day) coincided with the beginning of October, which became equinoctial day later on.[3]

Thibaut finds no authority in favour of Tilak's assertion that the term Viṣuvat means an equinox when the night and day are equal.

110. Th. discusses the meaning of Uttarāyaṇa and Dakṣiṇāyana. He rejects T.'s contention that they indicate the periods intervening between the equinoxes, and advises to accept them in the sense of the periods intervening between the solstices. He repeats that the spring of the *Brāhmaṇas* begins not with

1 *IA.*, 1895, p. 96 2 *Ibid.*, p. 96 3 *Ibid.*, p. 96

the vernal equinox, but at the point lying midway between winter solstice and equinox, and that ayanas are reckoned from the solstice. He rejects the explanation that "Uttarāyaṇa denotes the time when the sun is moving in the northern region and not towards the north."[1]

Thibaut rejects Tilak's contention that Uttarāyaṇa and Dakṣiṇāyana indicate periods between equinoxes.

111. On the strength of what has been said in paragraph 110, Th. draws the following conclusion: "As thus there is no trace of a year reckoned from the equinox in the *Brāhmaṇa*-period, there hardly seems a good reason for commencing the position of Kṛittikās at the head of the old lists of the *Nakshatras* with the vernal equinox."[2] Th. is unwilling to accept the interpretation of the position of the Kṛttikās, as indicated in the *Brāhmaṇas*, reflected afterwards in the *Jyotiṣa-Vedāṅga*, to the effect that the vernal equinox falls at 10° of Bharaṇī, a constellation between Aśvinī and Kṛttikās, and the latter constellation might be seen marking the equinox.[3]

Thibaut finds no reason for recognising vernal equinox being once in Kṛttikās.

112. In spite of the above argument, Th. does not rule out the possibility of Kṛttikās marking the position of the vernal equinox. He states that "It is, of course, not impossible that the old lists of the *Nakshatras* may really come down from the time when Kṛittikās marked the place of the vernal equinox, not only approximately, but accurately, i.e., about 2300 B.C. Only we must clearly realize that, in that case, astronomical views must be supposed to have prevailed at that time,[4] which greatly differed from those of the *Brāhmaṇa*-period; i.e., that people then must have looked on the vernal equinox as really marking the beginning of the year. That this was so is not impossible; but it has to be kept in view that it is an hypothesis not directly countenanced by anything in Vedic literature."[5] Th. repeats that Aśvinī, the leading asterism of later times, owed its position to its connection with equinox, but that cannot indicate that the ancient position of the Kṛttikās was due to an analogous cause.[6]

Thibaut does not altogether deny the hypothesis that Kṛttikās at the head of the old list of Nakṣatras marked the place of vernal equinox.

He rejects the hypothesis because it is not supported by anything in Vedic literature.

1 *Ibid.*, p. 96

2 *Ibid.*, p. 97

3 *Ibid.*, p. 97. This implies that Vedic literature is later than 2300 B.C. according to Th.

4 *I.e.* 2300 B.C.

5 *IA.*, 1895, p. 97

6 *Ibid.*, p. 97

Thibaut does not find any necessity in going back earlier than the time when winter solstice took place in Śraviṣṭhā.

113. Th. records his conclusions thus: "We arrive at the final conclusion that none of the astronomical data which so far have been traced in Vedic literature in any way compel, or even warrant us, to go back higher than the time when, the *Jyotisha Vedāṅga* explicitly states, the winter solstice took place in Śravishṭhās."[1] As to the exact period when this happened, Th. agrees with W. that "if all sources of possible error are taken into joint consideration, 'a thousand years would not be too long a period to cover all the uncertainties involved.' "[2] [Whitney, the *Lunar Zodiac*, p. 384][3].

Thibaut agrees with Tilak that the motions of the sun and the moon were determined, in ancient India, with reference to known fixed asterisms.

114. Th. agrees with T.'s observation (Ch. III of the *Orion*), that in the earliest days, the motions of the sun and the moon were determined with reference to known fixed stars. He points out at the same time, however, that "in Indian literature there appears to be from the very beginning a most confusing mixing up of constellations and divisions of ecliptic. Artificial systems, like that represented by the *Jyotisha Vedāṅga*, appear to have been established very early: I have no doubt that at the time, when the author of the 19th Book of the *Kaushītaki Brāhmaṇa* could say that the sun always turns towards the north on the new moon of Māgha, there already existed a fully worked out calendaric scheme, most probably very similar to that of the *Vedāṅga*. It appears probable that such a scheme was known at the time already when the months first received their names from the *Nakshatras* in which the moon was full."[4]

Thibaut criticises strongly the power of observation of early Indo-Aryan astronomers.

115. Immediately afterwards, Th. expresses his adverse opinion about the power of observation of the early Indo-Aryans. Says he that a distinction should be made "between minuteness and accuracy of astronomical observation on the one hand, and of arithmetical calculation on the other hand. The former cannot be presupposed for an early period—they, in fact, never existed in India ; but there stands nothing in the way of our admitting that the Hindus at a very early period already were capable of devising a purely theoretical subdivision of the sun's

1 *Ibid.*, p. 97
2 *Ibid.*, pp, 97, 98
3 *Ibid.*, p. 98 fn.
4 *Ibid.*, p. 98

and moon's path into twenty-seven equal parts, and accurately calculating the places occupied in those parts by the two heavenly bodies in all seasons and months of the year. There is no valid reason, in fact, to deny that what is actually done in the *Jyotisha Vedāṅga* and the *Sūrya Prajñapti* of the Jainas could be done at a much earlier period already. Each artificial scheme of that type, of course, requires, at least, one observation which provides a starting point for all calculations." Th. however is not sure what that original observation was ; it may have been winter solstice as in the *Jyotiṣa Vedāṅga* or it may be summer solstice.[1]

Thibaut states that ancient Indo-Aryans did not leave behind any systematic record as proof of their observations.

116. Th. tries to measure the value of observations by ancient Indo-Aryans. As to the accuracy of their observations, Th. is of opinion that this "was at no period a strong point of Hindu astronomers." Says Th., "We need only remember that even after the Hindus had reached a comparatively high stage of theoretical asronomical knowledge and probably cultivated systematic observation to some degree, they yet appreciated its importance so imperfectly as to leave no direct record of what they did ; astronomers tacitly corrected the astronomical elements they had received from their predecessors, but did not state what the observations were that appeared to call for those corrections."[2]

Th. further states: "It is very difficult to admit anything like even approximate correctness of observation," anterior to the period of the *Siddhāntas*. The only class of observations he allows the ancient Indo- Aryans is those of solstices. A correct result cannot be expected without repeated observations for a number of years, and a correct evaluation of a year of 365 days cannot be made by following this method[3].

Thibaut is of opinion that early Indo-Aryans had no notion of the proper length of the year, though they had some knowledge of intercalation.

Accusing the ancient Indo-Ayrans of being devoid of any approximately correct notion of the length of the year, Th. goes on to state that "what length was attributed to the year in the Vedic period we do not directly know ; for the ever-recurring statement as to the year having 360 days can hardly represent the entire knowledge of the Hindus of that time, and, moreover, there are positive indications of some system of intercalation (the 13th month, etc.), which no doubt improved matters to some extent. But in the next following period—represented by the *Jyotisha Vedāṅga*, Garga,

1 *Ibid.*, p. 98 2 *Ibid.*, p. 99 3 *Ibid.*, p. 99

etc.—we have most definite and circumstantial information as to the recognition of a solar year of 366 days, i.e., of a year three quarters of a day in fault. No clause, providing for a periodical correction of this fault, has been traced either in the *Jyotisha Vedāṅga* or any cognate work ; the need of such a correction was evidently not perceived, or certainly not regarded, for centuries. Now, it would hardly recommend itself to ascribe to the Hindus of the Vedic period, a more accurate knowledge of the length of the year than to their successors, and we therefore must assume, however unwillingly, that they also, at the best, valued solar year at 366 days."[1]

Thibaut states that not only in regard to equinox, but also in regard to solstice, the ancient Indo-Aryan observations cannot be depended upon.

117. Th. is not satisfied with simply stating that the ancient Indo-Aryans had no knowledge of equinoxes. He goes further and says that even in regard to solstices, their knowledge was not dependable. For, asks he, with what accuracy can solstices be observed by men who made the initial mistake in regard to the length of the year. He fails to understand, how any civilised nation, eager to maintain an orderly calendar, could tolerate a scheme based on the hypothesis of quinquennial yuga. In his opinion, violent corrections were made from time to time, but there was nothing like "a methodical correction of chronometrical and astronomical theories, such as results from continued methodical observation," in the pre-Hellenic period.[2] Th. thinks that when the famous astronomer Varāha Mihira (600 A, D.) made a survey of different Hindu systems of astronomy, he had before himself works of two different descriptions only—those that were based on Greek science, and those that were not superior to *Jyotiṣa-Vedāṅga.* "And when we note that he manifestly was acquainted only with two positions of the summer solstice,—*viz.*, the one belonging to his own period and the old traditional one recorded in the *Vedāṅga,* and that hence evidently there existed no record of an analogous observation from the whole period intervening between those two observations (a period of, let us say, 1700 years),[3] we shall feel neither inclined to form a high opinion of the skill of the people who made the earlier observation, nor to believe that

1 *Ibid.*, p. 99

2 *Ibid.*, pp. 99, 100

3 [*i.e.*, 600 A.D. and 1100 B.C.]

that observation was preceded by a series of older analogous observations and that records of these are embodied in ancient Hindu literature.[1]

E. Bühler's Arguments In support of Jacobi and Tilak

118. B. makes a careful examination of the arguments of both J. and T.[2], and then comes to the decision that "they have made good their main proposition, *viz*., that the Kṛittikā-series is not the oldest arrangement of the Nakshatras known to the Hindus, but that the latter once had an older one, which placed Mṛigaśiras at the vernal equinox. If this proposition has not been proved mathematically, it has at least been made probable:—so probable that it may be used as the foundation" of a chronology for earlier Vedic period.[3]

In Bühler's opinion both Jacobi and Tilak have been able to establish that the early Indo-Aryans had knowledge of Nakṣatra-series with Mṛgaśiras at its head.

1 *IA*., 1895, pp. 99, 100. The arguments of W. and Th. will be dealt with in subsequent paras.

2 B. mentions the surprising chance by which he came in contact with these two scholars. It was through J. that B. first came to know that there were statements in Vedic works, calculated to upset the prevailing theories regarding the age of the Veda. Whilst B. was journeying from Vienna to England in 1892, he stopped at Bonn (July 23) to call on J, his former companion during Tour in the Rajputana desert in the winter of 1873-74. J. assisted B. efficiently in his exploration of the libraries of Jesalmir and Bikanir. During the talks at Bonn, J. explained his own interpretation of VII. 103.9 of the *Rv*., and drew attention of B. to the significance of the statements of the *Brāhmaṇas* regarding the beginning and end of the year as well as regarding the beginning of the three seasons of four months each. The indications that the so-called Kṛttika-series were not the oldest arrangement of the Nakṣatras known to the Hindus were discussed at some length. B. congratulated J. for his discoveries.

Six weeks later, the Committee of the Ninth International Oriental Conference at London sent B. the *Orion* (Ms) of T. with a request to give his opinion for its being printed in the *Transactions*. He was surprised to find that T.'s views closely agreed with those of J., and that T. had quoted some of those passages that J. had discussed with him before. Though B. differed from T. in same details, he recommended its inclusion in its entirety, containing as it did, an important discovery. The *Transactions*, however, printed only an abstract of the *Orion*, for want of funds. In November of that year, B. received from T. 2 copies of the abstract—at Vienna. One of them was sent to J. B. informed him of T.'s discovery and of the submission of his larger work at the International Oriental Conference, London.—*IA*., 1894, p. 239

3 *IA*., 1894, p. 239

119. Before dealing with the points of J. and T., B. gives a summary of the principal arguments put forward by them thus:

Bühler's summary of the arguments of Jacobi and Tilak.

"While the arrangement of the Nakshatras according to the Kṛittikā-series places the winter solstice in the month of Māgha, the vernal equinox in Vaiśākha, the summer solstice in Śrāvaṇa and the autumnal equinox in Kārttika, there are a number of passages in Vedic works which contain contradictory statements. The well-known passages from the *Taittirīya Saṁhitā*, as well as from the *Kaushītaki* and *Pañchaviṁśa Brāhmaṇas*, to which Prof. Tilak, *Orion*, p. 67, adds one from the *Gopatha Brāhmaṇa*, and to which others might be added from the *Śrauta*[1] *Sūtras*, declares the full moon night of Phālguna to be 'the mouth of the year'. Moreover, another passage of the *Taittirīya Saṁhitā* asserts that Uttara Phalgunī is the first night of the year and Pūrva Phalgunī is the last, which assertions are repeated in figurative language by the author of the *Kaushītaki Brāhmaṇa*. From the first set of utterances both Prof. Jacobi and Prof. Tilak infer, as has been done by others before them, that in the Vedic times a year, beginning with the full moon of Phālguna, was used, and Prof. Jacobi alone points out that the second set of statements permits the inference that there was also a second year beginning exactly six months later in Praushṭhapada or Bhādrapada.

"The same scholar shows further that a third reckoning began with the month of Mārgasīrsha, which in the *Gṛihya Sūtras* and in Pāṇini's *Grammar* is called Āgrahāyaṇa or Āgrahāyaṇika, 'belonging to the beginning of the year'. Thus there are for the Vedic times three years, a Phālguna-year, six months later a Praushṭhapada-year, and again three months later a Mārgaśīrsha-year......... This is just what might be expected in a large country like India, which was cut up into numerous political and other divisions. But it seems to me that in the Vedic works there are other indications, such as the contradictory statements regarding the number of the seasons, showing that the reckoning of time even in the most early period was by no means uniform and that various opinions regarding astronomical matters prevailed.

1 See, e.g. *Āpastamba Śrauta-Sūtra*, V. 3. 16:
यत् फाल्गुनो-पूर्णमास आदध्यात् संवत्सरस्यैनमासन् दध्यात् द्व्यहे पुरैकाहे वा ॥
'If one kindles (*the sacred fire*) on the full moon day of Phālguna, one places it in the mouth of the year; (*hence one should do it*) two days or one day earlier."—*IA*., 1895, p. 239 fn,

"The question, which now arises, is what the astronomical position of the Nakshatras was, according to which the three initial months of these Vedic years were named. Do these years belong to the period when the colure of the equinoxes passed through Kṛittikā and Viśākhā and that of the solstices through Maghā and Śravaṇā? Or do they belong to an earlier time, when the colure of the solstices went through Uttara Phalgunī and Pūrva Bhādrapadā and that of the equinoxes through Mṛigaśiras and Mūla? In other words, do they belong to the time, when the series of the Nakshatras, counting from that at the vernal equinox, began with Kṛittikā, or from the period when Mṛigaśiras occupied that position?

"Both scholars decide for the latter assumption".[1]

120. According to B., what may be urged in favour of J. and T.'s views is that a rational explanation of early Indo-Aryans beginning their years with any of the three months Phālguna, Bhādra, Agrahāyaṇa as J. states, or with one month, Phālguna, as T. thinks, is possible only if we admit that the time indicated was when Mṛgaśiras was at the head of the Nakṣatra-series. In other words, it was the time when the solstices and equinoxes stood as follows:

Bühler states that the selection of the months (3 according to Jacobi and 1 according to Tilak), for the beginning of a year indicates that Vedic texts are speaking of the time when Mṛgaśiras was at the head of the Nakṣatra-series.

winter solstice fell in Phālguna,
vernal equinox in Jyaiṣṭha,
summer solstice in Bhādra,
autumnal equinox in Agrāhāyaṇa (Mārgaśīrṣa),

B. thinks that it is rational to hold that a year in those days could have commenced with any one of the four months mentioned above. Therefore, B. supports J.'s conception that different schools of priests or astronomers started the year with any of the three months, Phālguna, Bhādra, Agrahāyaṇa (Jyaiṣṭha not mentioned as the first month), and named the year as Hīmā, Varṣā or Śarad (Vasanta not mentiond) in accordance with the season in which the first month fell.

Now, it may be argued, as has been done by some scholars, that it was not the time when Mṛgaśiras was at the head of the Nakṣatra-series but the time when Kṛttikā was at the head of the Nakṣatra-series, to which the Vedic texts refer. In the latter case,

1 *IA.*, 1894, p. 240

as B. points out, the solstices and equinoxes would stand as follows:

winter solstice in Māgha,
vernal equinox in Vaiśākha,
summer solstice in Śrāvaṇa,
autumnal equinox in Kārttika.

In other words, the year would have commenced with Māgha, Śrāvaṇa, or Kārttika. But, as pointed out before, the Vedic texts refer to year-beginning with Phālguna, etc. There is no reason why the second months of the seasons, Himā, Varṣā, or Śarad, should be chosen for beginning a year at the time when Kṛttikā was at the head of the Nakṣatra-series. B. is therefore convinced that when the reference in the Vedic texts is to the month of Phālguna, Bhādra or Agrahāyaṇa, it is nothing but the Mṛgaśiras epoch, i.e., when Mṛgaśiras was at the head of the Nakṣatra-series.[1]

121. B. finds justification for the contention that, in ancient times, the month of Bhādra was once the month in which the summer solstice fell (i.e., the summer solstice took place when Mṛgaśiras was at the head of the Nakṣatra-series). Several rules connected with rites and sacrifices are cited by B. from J. and T.'s writings to prove J. and T.'s contentions. One of the rules is concerned with fixing the date of Upākaraṇa[2], for the *Gṛhya* and *Dharma Sūtras* give three different times for the commencement of Vedic study. The principal time for study in ancient India is held to be the rainy season. Most of the Vedic texts indicate that solemn opening of the annual session of the schools happened "on the appearance of the herbs", i.e., on the first days of the monsoon. The question naturally arises as to the reason why some Sūtrakāras have three different months—Āṣāḍha, Śrāvaṇa, Bhādra—as suitable times for commencing the study of the Veda. This seeming contradiction can be explained on the supposition that the rainy seasons indicated belonged to three different Nakṣatra epochs. Accordingly, if we hold that summer solstice appeared in Āsāḍha in Aśvinī apoch, in Śrāvaṇa in Kṛttikā epoch, and in Bhādra in Mṛgaśiras epoch, the said contradictions disappear[3].

The rules regarding Upākaraṇa indicate the continuance of Mṛgaśiras epoch, according to Jacobi.

1 *IA.*, 1894, pp. 240, 241

2 See paras 54 and 55 where J.'s views in regard to Upākaraṇa have been elaborately dealt with.

3 *IA.*, 1894, pp. 241, 242

122. B. states that "A second rule, which evidently places the month of Praushṭhapada-Bhādrapada at the summer solstice, and in the beginning of the rains, has been noticed by Prof. Jacobi alone".[1] He points out that the Jainas, the 'most ancient heterodox sect of India,' according to him, begin their Pajjusan[2] (Paryuṣaṇa) on the 4th or 5th day of Bhādrapada, and that the Pajjusan marks the old term of the retreat of the Jaina monks during the rainy season. All Indian ascetics, whether orthodox or heterodox, were and are still bound by their rules to put a stop to their wanderings during the Monsoon, and to devote the four rainy months, to study of their scriptures, to meditation, prayer and preaching, as the rules of their order may require.[3]

Bühler agrees with Jacobi that the Pajjusan ceremony of the Jaina monks indicating year-beginning fell in Bhādra and summer solstice.

"Pajjusan...is the true Varshāvāsa of the Jaina monks", and one of the beginnings mentioned by their scriptures dating from the time "when, in accordance with Mṛigaśiras-series of Nakshatras, Bhādrapada was the month of the summer solstice and of the rains[4]."

123. The third significant rule mentioned by T. alone is pointed out by B. It enjoins the performance of the holiest Śrāddha in Bhādrapada, "the pitṛiyāna during which time the sun in older times went down the equator must have come to be regarded, for some purposes at least, as commencing from the summer solstice. With the winter solstice occurring on the Phālgunī full-moon day, we shall have the summer solstice on the Bhādrapadī full-moon, so that the dark half of [the month of] Bhādrapada was the first fortnight in the Pitṛiyāna, understood as commencing on the summer solstice. It was thus pre-eminently the fortnight of the *pitṛis* or the manes: and *to this day*, every Hindu celebrates the feast to the manes in this fortnight. As far as I know no reason has yet been advanced why the dark half of Bhādrapada should be called the fortnight of the *pitṛis* (*pitṛi-paksha*) and why special feasts to the manes should be ordained at this particular

Bühler agrees with Tilak that the performance of the holiest Srāddha in the month of Bhādra is indicative of year-beginning in summer solstice.

1 *Ibid.*, p. 242

2 Spending the rainy season.—M. Williams ; *IA.*, 1894, p. 242

3 *IA.*, pp. 242, 243

4 *Ibid.*, p. 243, and p. 243 fn. : पर्युषणाकल्प निर्युक्ति, 2nd gāthā. (quoted by B.).

period of the year. With the winter solstice in the asterism of Uttarā Bhādrapadā, that is, when it occurred on the Phālgunī full-moon, the matter is simply and satisfactorily explained. For then the Dakṣhiṇāyana or summer solstice commenced on the dark half of Bhādrapadā and this fortnight therefore naturally became *first* fortnight in the *ayana* of the *manes*."[1]

Pointing out that Parsis also celebrate their feast to the manes at the same time, T. thinks this coincidence to be important inasmuch as they refer to the periods of antiquity when the Indian and the Iranian Āryas must have lived together.[2]

T. further states that the above explanation implies that the feast to the manes became permanently fixed at this time, with the result that when the vernal equinox receded to the Kṛttikās, the feasts still continued to be celebrated in the dark half of Bhādrapada.[3]

In the concluding chapter of the *Orion*, T. reverts to this subject, which is also noticed by B.[4] According to T., "an almost continuous record of the year-beginnings from the oldest time down to the present" is to be found in the literature of India. T. states that he has already referred to the "occurrence of the *pitṛi-paksha* in Bhādrapada as relic of the time when the year commenced with the Phalgunī full-moon. Our Shrāvaṇī ceremony appears to have been once performed in Bhādrapada (*Manu*, IV. 95) ; and as it marked the beginning of the rains, when the herbs appear anew (Āshvalāyana Gṛihya Sūtra, III. 5.2), we can here trace the recession of the rainy season from Bhādrapada to Shrāvaṇa and from Shrāvaṇa to Āṣhaḍha (Sāṅkhyāyana Br., I. 3) and finally from Āshādḥa to Jyaiṣhṭḥa, as at present, then fully corroborating the recession of the beginning of the year or the winter solstice from Chaitra to Phālguna, from Phālguna to Māgha, and from Māgha to Pauṣha."[5]

124. B. is of opinion that of all the arguments adduced by J. and T., those that are mentioned above are the strongest "to shew that the Vedic Phālguna, Prauṣhṭḥapada and Mārgaśīrṣa years began respectively with the winter and summer solstices

1 Tilak., *The Orion*, p. 91
2 *Ibid.*, pp. 91, 92
3 *Ibid*, p. 91 fn.
4 *IA.*, 1894, p. 243
5 *The Orion*, pp. 216, 217

Bühler states that Jacobi and Tilak have proved that traces of the time when Prauṣṭhapada coincided with winter solstice and Mṛgaśiras with equinox are found in Vedic writings.

and the autumnal equinox." B. thinks that what has been said "is quite sufficient to make it at least probable that some Vedic writings have preserved reminiscences of a time when the Nakṣhatra Prauṣhṭhapadā or Bhādrapadā stood at the winter solstice, and the vernal equinox fell in Mṛigaśiras, and that this arrangement has left its traces in the rules regarding the seasons for certain ceremonies and sacrifices." As to the time when this was correct, B. refers to J.'s table and finds the time to be 4420 B.C. "And if due allowance is made for possible and very probable errors of observation, the year 3800 B.C. may be fixed as the lowest term when a Mṛigaśiras-series could have been settled."[1]

125. B. firmly holds that "the arrangement of the Nakshatras with the Kṛttikās at the vernal equinox is an Indian invention."[2]

In Bühler's opinion, Kṛttikā-series is an Indian invention, and some Indo-Aryan rites and sacrifices had been prevalent long before the time of the Kṛttikā-series.

He points out that the position of Kṛttikā at the vernal equinox was "astronomically correct about 2550 B.C."[3] Therefore after the necessary allowance is made for errors owing to primitive method applied, one can safely assert that "ancient Hindus must have possessed an astronomical science," based on scientific principles and actual observations, and that "some of the Hindu riteș and sacrifices existed even before the time when the Kṛttikā-series was invented, and were settled long before 2000 B.C."[4]

II. A REVIEW OF THE OPINIONS OF DIFFERENT SCHOLARS

126. The statements contained in paras 59 to 125 are sufficiently clear to indicate the viewpoints of the different

1 *IA.*, 1894, pp. 244, 245

2 *Ibid.*, p. 245

3 2350 B.C. according to T.

B.'s astronomical adviser Dr. R. Schram says in a letter to B. : "The precession amounts at present to 50″ 23 annually or to 1° in 72 years. But it does not remain constant. Two thousand years ago it was about 46″ and thus we get the 78 years for a degree, entered in Prof. Jacobi's Table. It is a matter of course that also this figure is correct for a certain period only. It is impossible to give generally correct figures for long periods because the time, required for the passage through a whole degree, is variable."—*IA.*, 1894, p. 245 fn.

4 *IA.*, 1894, p. 245

scholars in regard to the antiquity of Vedic literature. In the following pages, it will first be examined how far the criticisms levelled against J. and T. by W. and Th. are justified in regard to what the former two scholars have stated, and then find out whether the views of J., T., and B. are correct.

Views of scholars.

A. ANALYSIS OF WHITNEY'S VIEWS

(a) Fulfilment by Tilak of Whitney's conditions

127. It has been pointed out before that W. admits the main thesis of T., viz., that "in the earlier times, the asterismal system began with Kṛittikās instead of Aśvinī."[1] This is however only a part of T.'s thesis. The other part, viz., that the ancient Indo-Aryans had knowledge of an older series with Mṛgaśiras at its head, is not admitted by W.[2] In respect of Kṛttikā-series, he denies that the Indo-Aryans were its discoverers. He strongly speaks against the astronomical knowledge of ancient Indo-Aryans and declares that they borrowed a true astronomical science only from the Greeks so late as first century A.D. W. emphasises that the Indo-Aryans can claim no credit for the different early systems indicating their antiquity.

Whitney admits the main thesis of Tilak, viz., that Indo-Aryans had knowledge of Kṛttikā-series but denies its Indian origin.

128, After disposing of what he thinks to be the main thesis of T., in the aforesaid way, W. refers to the important passages of the *Taitt.-Saṃ.* and *Tāṇḍya-Br.*,—important because they contain evidence as to the antiquity of Vedic literature. The passages deal with the time when the year-long Sattra, the Gavām-ayana, is to commence. Of the four different dates given,[3] T. picks up, according to W., two, viz., Citrā full-moon and 4 days before the full-moon of Māgha (which W. thinks to be the full-moon of Caitra). These dates are stated to indicate the time of composition of the *Taitt.-Saṃ.*, but W. is of opinion that the required data for establishing validity of T.'s views have not been supplied. He therefore finds no reason for accepting them unless three specific data[4] mentioned by him were supplied. These are being examined now.

Different times for the ceremony of consecration in the year-long Sattra, Gavām-ayana.

1 See para 85. 2 See para 83.
3 See para 85. 4 See para 86.

Datum I : Sattra is the counter-part of the year

129. It should be pointed out at the outset that W.'s statement that T. lost sight of Sattras other than Gavām-ayana etc. which lasted for different durations is not justified. For, T. warns his readers beforehand that his remarks are all applicable to year-long Sattras only, meaning thereby that they are not to be applied to other Sattras of which he had knowledge. "The idea of a sacrifice extending over the whole year may be safely supposed to have originated in the oldest days of the history of the Aryan race."[1]

Tilak was not ignorant of Sattras of different durations.

130. Sattra sacrifice in a particular form was the reflection of the year, says T. In this connection, he quotes p. 48 from Haug's Introduction to his edition of the *Aitareya-Brāhmaṇa*. "The *Satras*, which lasted for one year, were nothing but an imitation of the sun's yearly course. They were divided into two distinct parts ....In the midst of both was the *Vishuvan* i.e. the equator or the central day, cutting the whole Satra into two halves."[2] On this T. remarks: "When this course of sacrifices was thus completed, it was naturally found that the year also had run its course."[3]

Tilak, and Haug on Sattra as counterpart of the year.

131. An analysis of the component parts of the Sattra called Gavām-ayana[4] is given below to show how it was the counterpart of the year.

Component parts of Gavām-ayana as described by Tilak.

The rituals for the first 180 days.

Names of components	Duration
(1) Prāyaṇīya (introductory) Atirātra or opening day	1 day
(2) Caturviṃśa day. It is Agniṣṭoma or some sacrifice accompanied with *Ukthas* [eulogistic verses—all the strotras being in Caturviṃśa stoma (metre)]. It is also called *Ārambhanīya* (*Ait.-Br.*, IV, 12) or Prāyaṇīya (*Tāṇḍya-Br.*, IV. 2). This is the real beginning of the Sattra	1 day
(3) A group of rituals covering 5 months, each month consisting of 4 Abhiplava Ṣaḍahas	24 days
and 1 Pṛṣṭhya Ṣaḍaha	6 days
	30 days
So 5 months=30 × 5.............................	150 days

1 Tilak, *The Orion*, p. 14 2 *Ibid.*, pp. 11, 12 3 *Ibid.*, p. 12

4 "There are many annual *Sattras* like *Ādityānām-ayanam*, *Āṅgirasām-ayanam*, *Gavām-ayanam* etc., mentioned in the Brāhmaṇas and Shrauta

(4)	3 Abhiplavas i.e.	18 days	28 days which, with the 2 opening days at the beginning, complete the 6th month of 30 days
and	1 Pṛṣṭhya i.e.	6 days	
(5)	Abhijit day	1 day	
(6)	Svara-sāman days	3 days	
			180 days

The rituals (1) to (6) come in the reverse order for the subsequent 180 days.

(7)	*Viṣuvat*		
(8)	Svara-sāman days=	3 days	28 days, which with the 2 concluding days make the 7th month of 30 days
(9)	Viśvajit day (prepared with all the Pṛṣthyas) =	1 day	
(10)	1 Pṛṣṭhya i.e.	6 days	
	and 3 Abhiplavaṣ i.e.	18 days	

(11) 4 months
each month consisting of
1 Pṛṣṭhya Ṣaḍaha = 6 days
4 Abhiplava Ṣaḍahas = 24 days
30 days

4 months=4 x 30..................120 days

(12)	3 Abhiplava Ṣaḍahas	=18 days	
	1 Goṣṭoma	= 1 day	
	1 Āyuṣṭoma	= 1 day	
	Daśarātra	=10 days	30 days
(13)	Mahāvrata day corresponding to Caturviṃśa day Agniṣṭoma	=1 day	included in (9) and (10)
(14)	Udayanīya (concluding) Atirātra	=1 day	
			180 days

Total 360 days (i.e. the whole year[1])

Sūtras: and as observed by Dr. Haug, they seem to have been originally established in imitation of the sun's yearly course. They are the oldest of the Vedic sacrifices, and their duration and other details have been all very minutely and carefully noted down in the sacrificial works. All these annual *Sattras* are not, however, essentially different from each other, being so many different variations or modifications, according to circumstances, of a common model or type, and the *Gavām-ayanam* is said to be this type." Tilak, *The Arctic Home in the Vedas*, p. 193

1 The above chart has been prepared substantially in accordance with that given by T. in his *Arctic Home in the Vedas* (1903), p. 208. Cf. *Śatapatha-Br.*, (SBE), pt. 2 (1885), p. 427, and pt. 5 (1900), p. 139, fn. (Tr. by J. Eggeling); *Ṛgvedic Brāhmaṇas*, (Tr. by Keith), (containing Aitareya-Br. and Kauṣ.-Br., p. 6). The *Aitareya-Brāhmaṇa* contains the opinion that by holding the session called *Gavām-ayana*. they also hold *Ādityānām-ayana* (IV. 17).

The above analysis shows that all the days of the lunar year prevalent at the time were filled up with one or other part of the sacrificial activity. So when T. stated that the sacrifice and the year were synonymous he had aforesaid details in his mind.

Evidence that Sattra reflects the year.

132. The year has been identified with the Sattra in various *Brāhmaṇas*. For instance, (a) the *Aitareya-Brāhmaṇa* describes the sacrifice called Sattra as identical with year. It states that the different parts of the Sattra are related to the different parts of the year.

"Now they proceed to the Caturviṃśa[1] day in the beginning, by it they grasp year, consisting of 360 days. The introductory Atirātra is this side, and the concluding Atirātra the other side of the year. Ṣaḍaha consists of four sets of six days each, the first six representing six seasons, the first and the second set representing a year etc."[2]

(b) The *Kauṣī.-Br.* refers to the way the year is to be obtained, and identifies it with the sacrifice:

"The Atirātra is undertaken to obtain the year; Caturviṃśa being the beginning of the year is an agniṣṭoma which is the beginning of the sacrifice, and the year contains twenty-four half months and 360 days; and by performing the abhiplava the sacrificers mount the year."[3]

(c) The *Śatapatha-Brāhmaṇa* calls the year the deity to whom sacrifice is offered.[4] Another name of the year is Sattra. "The year indeed is man."[5] The different parts of the man's body are compared to the different parts of the Sattra, and thus the Sattra is equated to the year.

Gavām-ayana is counterpart of the year.

133. It is clear from the foregoing instances that it cannot be denied that the year-long Sattra was called the counter-part of the year. So the first datum of W. (see para 86) is established.

1 Sacrifice accompanied with eulogistic verses, which were in Caturviṃśa Stoma (metre) and were recited on that day.

2 Keith, *Ṛgvedic Brāhmaṇas* (1917), s. v. *Aitareya-Brāhmaṇa*, IV. 12; IV. 14; IV. 16; pp. 206-8

3 *Ibid.*, s. v. *Kauṣītaki-Brāhmaṇa*, XVII. 5; XIX, 8; XX. 1; pp. 412, 454, 457; Cf. XX. 2-4, pp. 458-460

4 Eggeling, *Śatapatha-Br.*, (S. B. E.), pt. 5, XII, I. 1. 1; 1.3.9 pp. 135, 141, etc.

5 *Ibid.*, XII, 2. 1.1; 2. 4. I; 3, 2, 1; pp. 144, 160, 168 etc. पुरुषो वै संवत्सरः ।

Datum 11: Viṣuvat stands for a point attached to the Equinox

The nature of Viṣuvat as described in the Śatapatha-Brāhmaṇa.

134. Anybody, following the component parts of *Gavām-ayana* (para 131), will find that item No. 7, the Viṣuvat, is placed after 180 days, just in the middle of 360 days, but no day is allotted to the same. It is therefore reasonable to infer Viṣuvat to be only a point and not a day.

The following extract from the *Śatapatha-Brāhmaṇa* shows how agitated the ancient Indo-Aryans were at one time over the nature of Viṣuvat.

तदाहुः यद्द्वादश मासाः संवत्सरस्याथैतदहरत्येति यद्वैषुवतमवरेषामेतात् परेषामित्यवरेषां चैव परेषां चेति ह ब्रूयादात्मा वै संवत्सरस्य विषुवानङ्गानि मासा यत्र वा आत्मा तदङ्गानि यत्रो अङ्गानि तदात्मा न वा आत्माङ्गान्यतिरिच्यते नात्मानमङ्गान्यतिरिच्यन्त एवमु हैतदवरेषां चैव परेषां च भवति ॥ XII. 2. 3. 6

अथ वा अतोऽह्नमभ्यारोहः प्रायणीयेनातिरात्रेणोदयनीयमतिरात्रमभ्यारोहन्ति चतुर्विंशेन महाव्रतमभिप्लवेन परमभिप्लवं पृष्ठ्येन परं पृष्ठ्यमभिजिता विश्वजितं स्वरसामभिः परान् स्वरसाम्नोऽथैतदहरनभ्यारूढं यद्वैषुवतमभि ह वै श्रेयांसं रोहति नैनं पापीयानभ्यारोहति य एवमेतद्वेद ॥ XII. 2. 3. 10

"As to this they ask, 'Seeing that there are the twelve months of the year, and that one day, to wit, the Viṣuvat, is in excess, does that belong to those (months) that go before or to those that follow.' Let him say, 'Both to those that go before and to those that follow; for Viṣuvat is the body (trunk) of the year, and the months are its limbs; and where the body is, there are (or that includes) also the limbs, and where the limbs are, there is also the body; and neither is the body in excess of the limbs, nor are the limbs in excess of the body; and thus indeed, that (day) belongs both to them (months) that go before and those that follow." XII, 2, 3. 6

"And in this way, indeed, there is an ascent of days:—by means of the opening Atirātra, they ascend the concluding Atirātra, by means of the Caturviṃsa the Mahāvrata, by means of Abhiplava a subsequent Abhiplava, by means of Pṛṣṭhya a subsequent Pṛṣṭhya, by means of Svara-Sāmans the subsequent Svara-Sāmans, but that one day is not ascended, to wit, the Viṣuvat." XII 2. 3. 10[1]

1 Keith also admits that "The middle day, the Viṣuvant, divides it (i.e. Sattra) into two halves", but does not explain how. See his *Religion and Philosophy of the Veda and Upanishads*, I, p. 350

135. As stated above, the *Śatapatha-Brāhmaṇa* leaves no room for doubt that Viṣuvat divided the year into two halves. The question arises, whether Viṣuvat divides the particular day, to which it is attached, into two halves. T.'s opinion is in the affirmative. He states: "Now, as *Vişhuvan* literally means the time when day and night are of equal length, if we suppose the year to have at the time commenced with the winter solstice, the Viṣhuvan or the equinoctial day could never have been its central day, and the middle day of the *Satra* would correspond, not with the equinoctial, as it should, but with the summer solstice......But if *Vişhuvan* was thus the central day of the year, the year must have once commenced with the equinoxes."[1]

Viṣuvat divided the year into two halves.

136. The passages quoted above indicate that Viṣuvat belongs to both the halves (each of 180 days) of the Sattra or the year, instead of belonging exclusively to one or the other half. If so, then the Viṣuvat must be attached to the last day of the first part consisting of 180 days, and the first day of the next part consisting of 180 days. Now, according to the context, one order of the sacrifice is finished on the completion of the 180th day, and the reverse order of the same begins immediately afterwards and is finished like the first order on the 180th day. So, in point of fact, Viṣuvat cannot be a whole day or even part of a day, but is a point attached to a particular day, the central day. This is the reason why the *Śatapatha* or other *Brāhmaṇas* do not put a day for Viṣuvat, even though at the time of mentioning it they call it Viṣuvat day.

Viṣuvat is only a point attached to the central day.

As to the position occupied by Viṣuvat as a point, W. has correctly placed it between "180 days of ceremonies in a certain order preceding it and 180 days of the same in a reverse order following it."[2] In other words, Viṣuvat is that point which falls after the last 12 hours of the first 180 days and before the first 12 hours of the following 180 days. In that case, it makes the day portion and the night portion of the day to which it is attached equal. Therefore, Th.'s assertion that "Vishuvat day is simply the central day of the sacrifice wherever that day may fall"[3] is

1 Tilak, *The Orion*, p. 21
Viṣuvat = having or sharing both sides equally.—Mon.-Williams, *Dict.*, p. 998

2 *IA.*, 1895, p. 367

3 *Ibid.*, p. 96

without any foundation. Viṣuvat indeed is equinox, in which day and night are equal.

Datum III. Determination of the commencement of the year in Vedic times

137. When weighing the divergent views of scholars on the commencement of the year in Vedic times, it should be remembered that they differed as to the extent of astronomical knowledge of the ancient Indo-Aryans. W. and Th. on the one hand held that their astronomical knowledge was meagre and that the little of astronomy left by them is replete with inaccuracies. J. and T. on the other hand maintained a contrary view, attaching much importance to the findings of the ancient Indo-Aryans in this respect. This was supported by B.

Divergent views of scholars on year-beginning,

138. The rites and ceremonies in Vedic times bear evidence to the fact that there was a vigilant priestly class who engaged themselves throughout the year in a meticulous observation of the course of the sun, the moon and the Nakṣatras. In this way they settled the appropriate and auspicious moments and periods for the sacrifices and other religious ceremonies. The welfare of the society as also of the individuals was the object that could thus be achieved.

In the field of astronomy, observation of the heavens by ancient Indo-Aryans was careful and unremitting.

139. The twelve months that constituted a year had two sorts of names, according to the *Brāhmaṇas*. One set was as follows: Madhu-Mādhava (Phālguna-Caitra), Śuci-Śukra (Vaiśākha-Jyaiṣṭha), Nabhas-Nabhasya (Āṣāḍha-Śrāvaṇa), Īsa-Ūrja (Bhādra-Āśvina), Sahasa-Sahasya (Kārttika-Agrahāyaṇa), Tapas-Tapasya (Pauṣa-Māgha).[1] Another set of names is based on a principle that prevails even to this date. It is concerned with naming each month after a particular Nakṣatra when the same was seen as the background of the full-moon. The months were thus named after the 12 Nakṣatras followed in each case by the term Pūrṇamāsaḥ—Phalgunī, Citrā, Viśākhā, Jyeṣṭhā, Āṣāḍhā, Śravaṇā, Bhādrapadā, Aśvinī, Kṛttikā, Mṛgaśiras, Puṣyā, and Maghā. T. states that "months in the Hindu calendar receive their names from the full-moon nights occurring in them."[2]

The twelve months in Vedic times.

1 *Taitt.-Saṃ.*, IV. 4.11.1

2 *The Orion*, p. 76. The month begins with full moon, according to T.

The second set of names of the months is more frequently used in the *Brāhmaṇas*. This was due to the fact that gradually the Nakṣatras came to occupy a more and more important place in the life of ancient Indo-Aryans.

Important role of 27 Nakṣatras in the life of ancient Indo-Aryans.

140. The *Ṛgveda* speaks of Nakṣatras in general terms in more than one place. The 27 Nakṣatras on the ecliptic along the course of the sun around the earth were closely observed by the ancient Indo-Aryans. In sacrifices, in commencement of the study of the Vedas, in marriage ceremonies, and in rites connected with war, the Nakṣatras were consulted.

Below have been given the names of 27 Nakṣatras for facility of reference.[1]

The Nakṣatras in the Ṛgveda.

141. Some of the 27 Nakṣatras are mentioned with modified names in the *Ṛgveda*. They are

(1) Arjunī (i.e. Phalgunī),
(2) Aghā (i.e. Maghā),
(3) Tiṣya (i.e. Puṣyā),
(4) Mṛga (i.e. Mṛgaśiras) and
(5) Ahirbudhnya (i.e. Bhādrapadā).

Examples:

सूर्याया वहतुः प्रागात् सविता यमवासृजत् ।
अघासु हन्यन्ते गावोरर्जुन्योः परि उह्यते ॥

Rv., X. 85. 13

The dowry of Suryā (sun, as feminine) was sent by Savitṛ (Sūryā's father) on the occasion of her marriage. At the Aghā, the cows were killed, at the Arjunīs, she (the wife) is led round the fire.

प्र तद्विष्णुः स्तवते वीर्येण मृगो न भीमः कुचरो गिरिष्ठाः ।
यस्योरुषु त्रिषु विक्रमणेष्वधिक्षियन्ति भुवनानि विश्वा ॥

Ṛv., I. 154. 2

1 (1) Aśvinī, (2) Bharaṇī, (3) Kṛttikās, (4) Rohiṇī, (5) Mṛgaśiras. (6) Ādrā, (7) Punarvasu, (8) Puṣyā, (9) Aśleṣā, (10) Maghā, (11) Pūrva-Phalgunī, (12) Uttara-Phalgunī, (13) Hastā, (14) Citrā, (15) Svātī, (16) Viśākhā, (17) Anurādhā, (18) Jyeṣṭhā, (19) Mūlā, (20) Pūrva-Āṣāḍhā, (21) Uttara-Āṣāḍhā, (22) Śravaṇā, (23) Śraviṣṭhā (Dhaniṣṭhā), (24) Śatabhiṣaj, (25) Pūrva-Bhādrapadā, (26) Uttara-Bhādrapadā, (27) Revatī.

There are verses in the *Ṛgveda* treating of Nakṣatras and of natural phenomena generally, such as Uṣā, Saramā, etc.

That Viṣṇu is glorified, who by his prowess is (in) the dreadful Mṛga, (in) the lower region. In Viṣṇu's three paces all the worlds abide. (Cf. *Ṛv.*, I. 161. 16 ; X. 86)

Besides the aforesaid 5 Nakṣatras, there is no mention of any other in the *Ṛgveda.* For this silence, it would be incorrect to infer that the ancient Indo-Aryans had no knowledge of the remaining Nakṣatras. There is a Purānic story that the Moon had 27 Nakṣatras as his wives and that he spent one day in a month with each of them. This statement has resemblance to the remark contained in the following Ṛgvedic verse:

अथो नक्षत्राणामेषामुपस्थे सोम आहितः ॥ X. 85. 2

Then Soma, the moon, is placed in the lap of the Nakṣatras.

The verse does not indicate the number of Nakṣatras but it cannot be denied that it refers to a cluster of same.

12 out of 27 Nakṣatras used for 12 months.

142. Only 12 out of 27 Nakṣatras along the ecliptic have been selected in the *Brāhmaṇas* for attaching names to 12 months of the year. These are: Phalgunī, Citrā, Viśākhā, Jyeṣṭhā, Āṣāḍhā, Śravaṇā, Bhādrapadā, Aśvinī, Kṛttikā, Mṛgaśiras, Puṣyā, and Maghā. 27 Nakṣatras are thus divided into 12 groups, each having one of the above Nakṣatras at its head, and containing $2\frac{1}{4}$ Nakṣatras on an average.

Measurement of each of the 12 groups on an average.

A complete revolution of the moon around the earth in a month crosses the 27 Nakṣatras or 360.° Each Nakṣatra therefore covers $360° \div 27 = 13\frac{1}{3}$.° Hence each group of $2\frac{1}{4}$ Nakṣatras extends over $13\frac{1}{3} \times 2\frac{1}{4}$ or 30.°

This interval of 30° can now be measured in terms of years. According to modern astronomy the annual rate of the Precession of the Equinox is 50·23 seconds, which means that the precession takes 72 years[1] to cover 1.° Therefore each group of $2\frac{1}{4}$ Nakṣatras will take (72 × 30 or) 2160 years, approximately 2000 years, to run a course of 30.° The passage through a whole degree has been found by astronomers to be variable. So the duration of a Nakṣatra group or of a Nakṣatra epoch may be more or less than

1 See J.'s Supplementary Table in para 77. See also para 125 fn. for Schram's opinion as to the variability of the passage of a Nakṣatra through a degree.

2000 years. In J.'s Table, 78° is allotted to each group, making the complete circle possible in 2340 years.

The reason why the number of seasons in the *Ṛgveda* is differently stated to be 3, 5, 6 and 7.

143. Both W. and Th. did not obviously comprehend the Vedic method of computing seasons of a year, and erroneously thought that mention of 3, 5, 6 and 7 seasons[1] in the *Ṛgveda* was without any foundation. Viewed in the light of the explanation given by T., the ancient Indo-Aryans are found to have taken cognition of the fact that the number of seasons changed according to circumstances. T. states that their original home had only three major climatic changes for which they reckoned three seasons—Himā, Varṣā, and Śarad—in a year, each being 4 months approximately, and that as they advanced towards and within India, they were more and more in contact with further changes in the climate which led them to renumber the seasons at 5, viz., 3 seasons mentioned above plus Grīṣma, Vasanta. This however inconvenienced them, because a division of the 12 months of a year by 5 leaves a fraction of a month behind. So, at the next stage they took to division of the year into 6 seasons, all of equal duration. They are those named before as well as Hemanta in between Śarad and Himā Afterwards, it was found that as the year was lunar and consisted of 360 lunar days, it fell short of the full solar year i.e. (366 solar days), by 12 days, to be added to converted 354 solar days of the lunar year. The means adopted at first for bridging the gap was an addition of 12 days after the lapse of each year, as has been shown in the treatment of Ṛbhus in a previous para.[2] In course of time this was given up, and 30 days were added to every two and half years. This intercalated month was considered to constitute the 7th season.

What the leadership of Nakṣatra-series means.

144. It has been stated above that epochs named after particular Nakṣatras were recognized during the Vedic period. Thus Punarvasu-series, Mṛgaśiras-series, Kṛttikā-series, etc. meant only that Punarvasu, Mṛgaśiras, Kṛttikā, etc. were successively the heads of the 27 Nakṣatras. The change of leadership of the Nakṣatra-series

1 W. States: "With their customary looseness in regard to such matters the ancient Hindus reckoned three, or five, or six, or even seven seasons in the year".—*IA.*, 1895, p. 363

2 See para 31.

synchronised with the end of one Nakṣatra eopch and the beginning of another.

The term *Mukham* and its meaning.

145. One term has been repeatedly used in Vedic literature, viz, *mukham*, to express leadership, whether of the Nakṣatras, or of the seasons, or of the months in a year, To state that a particular Nakṣatrā was *mukham* (नक्षत्राणां मुखम्) is to signify the leadership of that particular Nakṣatra over the 27 Nakṣatrεs. Similarly, to call a particular month or season *mukham* of the year means that it was first of the months and seasons respectively of the year.

Evidence regarding Mṛgaśiras epoch and Kṛttikā epoch.

146. T. states that there are many passages in the *Taittirīya-Saṃhitā*, the *Taittirīya-Brāhmaṇa*, and other works "where the Kṛttikās occupy the first place in the list of the Nakshatras."[3] Many of these passages have been dealt with by the scholars. They point to the fact that Kṛttikā was the leader of the Nakṣatras at the time, and it was Kṛttikā epoch.

Kṛttikās are not mentioned in the *Ṛgveda* obviously for the reason that the period of the composition of the *Ṛgveda* ended long before the Kṛttikā-epoch. There are references to Mṛgaśiras at several places in the *Ṛgveda*—for instance, the hymns on the Ṛbhus, and on Vṛṣākapi.

There is a number of mentions of Kṛttikās as the head of the Nakṣatra-series in the *Brāhmaṇas*. This fact led T. to point out that the references to Kṛttikās as *mukham* were not accidental. Hints are available in the *Ṛgveda*, pointing to the prevalence of Mṛgaśiras epoch. In dealing with the Ṛbhus in a previous paragraph (19), it was pointed out that the story of the Ṛbhus found in the *Ṛgveda* establishes that the year commenced with the vernal equinox in Canis Major. For facility of reference, the translation of the passage, *Ṛv.*, I, 161. 13 is given below: "Oh Ṛbhus! you were asleep ; therefore ask Agohya[4] who is it that woke us up. The He-goat[5] declared the hound to be the awakener. As the year

1 *Taitt.-Saṃ.*, IV. 4. 10: कृत्तिकास्वग्निमादधीत……मुखं वा नक्षत्राणां यत्कृत्तिकाः।

One should consecrate the (sacred) fire in Kṛttikās.........Kṛttikās are the mouth of the Nakṣatras.

2 *Taitt.-Br.*, III. 1.1.6 and I. 5.1, 2

3 Tilak, *The Orion*, p. 39

4 One who cannot be concealed i.e. the sun.

5 The word used is वस्तो meaning he-goat (the sun).

is passed, you declare the same." The hound mentioned above is none other than the Canis Major of the constellation Orion (Mṛgaśiras). It is clear from this extract that the *commencement of the year synchronises with the appearance of Mṛgaśiras in the sky.*

Moreover, in the Vṛṣākapi hymn[1] (*Rv.*, X. 86), a reference to Mṛga or Mṛgaśiras is found in verse 22, the translation of which by T. is as follows: "Oh mighty Vṛṣākapi! when you rising upwards (or rather northwards) would come to (our) house, where would that great sinner Mṛga be? Where he, who misleads[2] people, would go?"[3] Here Vṛṣākapi is identical with the sun at the autumnal equinox and Mṛga with Mṛgaśiras. This was the commencement of the Mṛgaśiras epoch.[4]

The solution of the supposed anomaly concerning the 4 different dates for Initiation of Gavām-ayana in the *Brāhmaṇas.*

147. It is now clear that when a change in the leadership of Nakṣatras took place it was observed by those who were in charge of year-long sacrifices, and that some of the results of these observations are reflected in Vedic literature. This required a regular and prolonged observation of the heavens. The 4 different dates for the Initiation Ceremony of Gavām-ayana are to be taken as prevalent in different Nakṣatra epochs, and not in one,

148. T. states:—"All our measurements of time are directly based upon the changes in the positions of heavenly bodies. But there is no measurement of time, at present determined, which is longer than the period during which the equinoxes complete their revolution in the ecliptic. It is, therefore, the best measurement of time for determining the periods of antiquity, only if we have reliable records about the position of heavenly bodies in early days. Fortunately, such records of the time, when the Hellenic, the Iranian and the Indian Aryans lived together, have been preserved for us in the Rigveda...Commencing with the passages in the Taittirīya-Sanhitā and the Brāhmaṇas, which declare that the Phalgunī full-moon was once the new year's night, we found that Mrigaśhiras was designated by a name which, if rightly interpreted, showed that the vernal

Tilak explains the significance of year-beginning with Phalgunī and Citrā full moons.

1 See para 35. T. has successfully attempted to show that the hymn on Vṛṣākapi and that on the Ṛbhus demonstrate the familiarity of ancient Indo-Aryans with the Mṛgaśiras-series.

2 This means that at sunrise the Mṛga can no more be seen as it goes out of view in sunlight.

3 See para 39.

4 See para 42.

equinox coincided with that asterism in olden times. This was, so to speak, a sort of corroborative evidence of the truth of the statement in the Taittirīya-Sanhitā. A reference to the figure will show at a glance that if the sun be at the winter solstice on the Phalgunī full moon day, the moon to be full must be diametrically opposite to the sun and also near Phalgunī. Uttarā Phalgunī will thus be at the summer solstice and the vernal equinox will coincide with Mrigashiras. With the solstice in Maghā, the equinox will be in the Krittikās; while when the Uttarāyaṇa begins in Pausha, the equinox is in Ashvinī. Ashvinī and Pausha, Krittikās and Māgha, and Mrigashiras and Phālguna are thus the correlative pairs of successive year-beginnings depending entirely upon the precession of the equinoxes; and the facts, statements, texts, and legends,...supply us with reliable evidence, direct and indirect, of the existence of all these year-beginnings, in the various periods of Aryan civilisation."[1]

Following the *Taitt.-Saṃ.* which records another year-beginning with Citrā full-moon, T. compares it with Phalgunī full-moon and finds that vernal equinox would be at Punarvasu.[2] T. remarks that "the traces of such period which we can discover in the sacrificial literature and especially the express mention in Taittirīya-Sanhitā that the Chitrā full-moon once commenced the year are, in my opinion, sufficient to prove the existence of such a calendar in the primitive days."[3]

Tilak supplies evidences for proving the 3 data as demanded by Whitney,

149. It is now evident from the foregoing paras 129 to 148 that T. has supplied the data for proper interpretation of the passages from the *Taitt.-Saṃ.* and *Tāṇḍya-Br.* These are

(1) Sattra reflects the year.

(2) Viṣuvat, as a point, is attached to a day, the bright portion of which is equal to the dark portion, and is therefore an equinox (in which the day and the night are equal).

(3) The only cogent explanation of year-beginning at 4 different dates as described in the *Taitt.-Saṃ.* and *Tāṇḍya-Br.* lies in the fact that they were recognised as such in different Nakṣatra epochs.

1 Tilak, *The Orion*, pp. 199, 200
2 *Ibid.*, p. 200
3 *Ibid.*, p. 205

(b) Jacobi's statement justified

Jacobi states that year-beginning at Uttarā Phalgunī and year-end at Pūrvā Phalgunī are warranted by Vedic literature.

150. In criticising J. 's contention that the *Brāhmaṇas* fixed the year-beginning at Uttara-Phalgunī, W. states that the *Brāhmaṇas* had no pretence to such astronomical exactitude as would draw a line between the former and the latter Phalgunīs.

According to him, the ancient Indo-Aryans were not very particular in choosing the month from which the year was to begin, and there was no fixed month for the purpose. This is the reason why different dates of year-beginning are found in the *Taitt.-Saṃ.* and *Tāṇḍya-Br.*[1]

Apart from the arguments advanced by T. against this view, J. does not think that any month of the year was appropriate in the opinion of the ancient Indo-Aryans for commencement of the year. He has discussed this point while dealing with Frog song[2] of the *Ṛgveda* and Upākaraṇa ceremony mentioned in the Sūtras, arriving at the conclusion that there were three kinds of year-beginning in Vedic times. Of these, within the month of Phālguna, one year ends and the other year begins. So the line, lying between Uttarā Phalgunī and Pūrvā Phalgunī, divides the two consecutive years.

Whitney does not adduce any evidence that ancient Indo-Aryans borrowed their astronomicai system from the Greeks.

151. W. accuses J. of want of candour, because the latter has not openly stated that the ancient Indo-Aryans learnt about equinox from the Greeks or may be from the Chinese or the Arabians, and that they replaced Mṛgaśiras by Kṛttikās at the head of the Nakṣatra-series in imitation of the Greeks. W. has no hesitation in admitting the antiquity of the astronomical discoveries of Mesopotamia, China etc. but advises caution in regard to India.

W. does not deny that prior to the recognition of Aśvinī as the head of the Nakṣatra-series, the ancient Indo-Aryans had been familiar with Kṛttikās as the head of the series, but the Kṛttikā-system, according to him, was not an Indian invention. W. puts forward no evidence in support of this point.

1 See para 80.

2 See para 74.

Whitney's statement that non-mention of planets in the *Ṛgveda* implying Indo-Aryans' ignorance about them is not valid.

152. W. holds that as there is no mention of planets in the *Ṛgveda*, the Indo-Aryans were ignorant of same. This argument is invalid as no such inference can be drawn from silence.

B. Why Jacobi and Tilak's view should prevail against that of Thibaut's

Thibaut analyses Tilak's theory of year-beginning.

153. An elaborate criticism of the view of J. and T. has been made by Th.,[1] the major portion of which is devoted to an examination of their theories on year-beginning.

Th. starts by explaining the texts of the *Taitt-Saṃ.* and *Tāṇḍya-Br.*, which he himself renders into English.[2] Th.'s remarks on the views of J. and T. as to the dates for the beginning of Gavāmayana have already been given. In the light of what J. and T. have said and also otherwise, Th.'s remarks are being examined now. According to Th., the year-beginnings as shown by T. are as follows:

(1) The year begins with the full-moon of Māgha indicating summer solstice in Maghās agreeing with Kṛttikās as the head of the Nakṣatras, and with vernal equinox in Kṛttikā in 2350 B. C.[3] during which time the abovementioned two treatises were composed;

(2) The year begins also with full-moon of Phālguna indicating occurrence of winter solstice in 4000 B. C.;[4]

(3) The year begins also with the full-moon of Caitra indicating the winter solstice in 6000 B.C.[5]

Winter solstice in Śraviṣṭhā is the earliest limit for the date of the Vedas, according to Thibaut.

154. Both J. and T. consider that the above-mentioned three dates point to different year-beginnings at different epochs.[6] But this is not acceptable to Th. He wants it to be precisely proved that no alternative interpretation of the passages of the *Taitt-Saṃ.* and *Tāṇḍya-Br.*, other than the one given by T., is possible.[7]

Th. states that he will not be justified in dismissing altogether as impossible the conclusions reached by J. and T., as Vedic

1 *IA.*, 1895, pp. 85-100: "On some recent attempts to determine the antiquity of Vedic civilisation."

2 See para 88 for the translation of the passage. 3 See para 89.

4 & 5 See para 89. 6 See para 91. 7 See para 91.

civilisation and literature might be considerably older than hitherto supposed. But this statement has been contradicted by Th. himself when he finally says that some astronomical data in Vedic literature do not warrant the fixation of the date of the Vedas previous to the time when winter solstice took place in Śraviṣṭhā (i. e. 1100 B. C.).

Thibaut takes help of the *Kauṣ.-Br* (XIX. 2.3) for proper interpretation of passages in the *Taitt.-Saṃ.* and *Tāṇḍya-Br.*

155. Th. then takes up a passage from the *Kauṣītaki-Brāhmaṇa,* (XIX. 2.3),[1] because he thinks that if the passages from the *Taitt.-Saṃ.* and *Tāṇḍya-Br.* are not supplemented by the one from the *Kauṣ-Br.*, a proper interpretation of the former two passages is not possible. He further thinks that if this passage had not escaped the notice of T., a different conclusion regarding the antiquity of the Vedas might have been drawn.[2]

According to Thibaut there were two different dates for commencing the Gavām-ayana.

156, Th. reduces three different dates mentioned in the *Kauṣ-Br.* into two for beginning the Gavām-ayana.[3] Instead of the Śukla-pratipads (the first day after the new moon) of the months of Pauṣa, Māgha, and Caitra, he considers those of Pauṣa and Caitra as acceptable, leaving out Māgha.[4] He also states that the *beginning* of the *first day of the light half* (i.e. Śukla pratipad) and *end* of the *last day of the dark half* (i.e. amāvasyā) have each equal right to be called amāvasyā (new moon day).[5] The consideration of the beginning of the Śukla-pratipad and end of amāvasyā being equivalent to amāvasyā is due to the fact that he thinks that strictness of terminology should not be expected from the *Brāhmaṇas.*

Thibaut adds 29 days to Śukla-pratipad of Pauṣa, but not to that of Caitra without giving any reason.

157. As to why Th. takes only two different dates and not three for the commencement of Gavām-ayana, the explanation given by him is this: In interpreting this portion of the passage from the *Kauṣ.-Br.*, though he mentions the Śukla-pratipad as the beginning of Gavām-ayana, he adds 29 days to it before the real commencement of the sacrifice, These 29 days are necessary, according to him, for Dīkṣā (initia-

1 See para 92, where the original text and its translation have been given.

2 See para 92.

3 See para 93.

4 See para 94.

5 See para 95.

tion, 17 days) and Upasads, (12 days).[1] The sacrifice proper, says he, begins in Śukla-pratipad of Māgha, when the sun is said to be resting. Th. points out that this is winter solstice. In regard to Śukla-pratipad of Caitra he does not add 29 days for Dīkṣā and Upasads, thereby the sacrifice has to take place within Caitra and not in the next month Vaiśākha. He does not explain why he adds 29 days in the case of Pauṣa and not in the case of Caitra. This is an inconsistency.

158. Th. thinks that the date for commencement of the Sattra was shifted from Māgha to Caitra. He explains this by stating that the original intention of the ancient Indo-Aryans was to begin the Sattra at winter solstice, but in course of time this was discontinued and was replaced by a new and more convenient beginning (as regards rain, cold, etc.) in Caitra. This explanation by Th. was necessary because otherwise he would have had to admit that the different dates for commencing the Sattra pointed to their prevalence in different Nakṣatra epochs, which was opposed to his intention. Moreover, after stating that the Sattra reflects the year in a previous portion of his arguments he now goes against his own opinion expressed before by saying that the beginning of the Sattra had no connection with the commencement of the year at solstice.[3]

It is Thibaut's view that originally the year commenced at winter solstice, and that it was in Śraviṣṭhā,

Th. supports his conclusion by a reference to the passage quoted from the *Kauṣ.-Br.* (XIX. 2.3) and states that there is a definite remark in this important passage of the *Brāhmaṇa* implying that the winter solstice coincided with ihe new moon of Māgha.[4] He believes that this indicates the date of the *Kauṣ.-Br.*, because the *Vedānga-Jyotiṣa* also speaks of winter solstice at the beginning of the bright half of Māgha. This was, according to him, no other winter solstice than the one in Śraviṣṭhā. On this ground, he places the *Kauṣ.-Br.* with the *Vedāṅga-Jyotiṣa* at the late date 1100 B.C. This statement is obscure because the solstice in Śraviṣṭhā is not winter, but summer solstice. six months apart from winter solstice in Māgha.

159. Th. then examines the passages of the *Taitt.-Saṃ* and *Tāṇḍya-Br.* to see whether it is possible to interpret them in an

1 See para 98.
2 See para 99.
3 See para 99.
4 See para 99.

Thibaut takes the 4 dates cited in the *Taitt.Saṃ* and *Tāṇḍya-Br.* to belong to a period near to the *Kauṣ. Bṛ.*

analogous way and thus connect them with a period, not distant from the *Kauṣ.-Br.*[1] He finds that the different dates for the Dīkṣā of Gavām-ayana are only optional, being prevalent at one and the same time. The effect of this interpretation is to nullify the possibility of placing each of the different dates at equinox for the performance of the annual Dīkṣā of the yearly Sattra in different Nakṣatra epochs, viz., Mṛgaśiras and Kṛttikās, as warranted by the texts, and explained by J. and T., and supported by B,

The meaning of the statement that Phālguna full-moon is the mouth of the year, according to Thibaut.

160. Next, Th. explains what is meant by the words in the text, viz. that full-moon in Phalgunī is the mouth, i.e., the beginning of the year. This, or the closely related one 'the (month) Phālguna is the mouth of the year' occurs in numerous places of the *Brāhmaṇas.*

Thibaut tries to prove that Phalgunī full moon did not coincide with the vernal equinox.

The *Jyotīṣa-Vedāṅga* is taken by Th. to be the guide to determine the date of the *Kauṣ.-Br.*, but no explanation is given as to why the *Jyotiṣa-Vedānga* should be considered as the determinant of the dates of the aforesaid Vedic treatises. The basis on which Th. works up his theory, viz., that for all time in ancient India, solstices were looked upon as marking the beginning of the year[2] does not bear scrutiny. He cites the authority of the *Jyotiṣa-Vedānga* and *Kauṣ-Br.* to prove that the day following the new moon is the date on which the Sattra and therefore the year commenced. He tries to reconcile this with the full-moon mentioned in the *Taitt.-Saṃ.* and the *Tāṇḍya.-Br.* in a circuitous way. Attempts have been made by him to connect year-beginnings with the Cāturmāsya sacrifices and thereby to avoid the need for linking the year-beginning with the equinoxes. Th. next considers which of the three 4-monthly groups should be taken as the first one. In view of the fact that the *Brāhmaṇas* always mention Vaiśvadeva as the name for the first group of the three 4-monthly sets along with Phalgunī Pūrṇamāsaḥ (or Citrā Pūrṇamāsaḥ) indicating warm season, Th. concludes that the Cāturmāsya commenced in that season, and therefore Phālguna was called the mouth of the year in the *Brāhmaṇas.*[3]

1 See para 100. 2 See para 101. 3 See para 101.

The commencement of Cāturmāsya sacrifices in the warm season leads Thibaut to make the wrong inference that the year commenced with Phālguna, but had no connection with the equinox.

In this connection, Th. refers to the passage from the *Kauṣ-Br.* quoted by him, to prove that the mouth or beginning of the year had no connection with vernal equinox. For, the new moon (amāvasyā) preceding Māghī full-moon mentioned in the aforesaid passage of the *Kauṣ-Br.* coincides, according to Th., with the winter solstice and the Cāturmāsya sacrifice in the full-moon was held a month and a half after the winter solstice, which Th. connects with the month of February (Phālguna). Thus there is a long gap between the winter solstice and the first day of the Cāturmāsya, *which Th. looks upon as year-beginning.*[1] The connection of year-beginning with equinox, on the other hand, as has been shown before, is coincident.

The fact that solstices by their characteristics are in a more favourable position to draw the attention of ancient Indo-Aryan observers does not necessarily indicate, as Th. opines, that the detection of the equinoxes by observation was for them an impossibility. On the other hand, the repeated minute observation of the heavens led them to many discoveries like the succession of one Nakṣatra epoch by another, the intercalary thirteenth month, etc. An analysis of the year-long Sattra has shown that the ancient Indo-Aryans knew of 2 days in the Sattra, in each of which the bright portion was equal to the dark portion or in other words the two equinoxes. His opinion that the ancient Indo-Aryans were not familiar with equinoxes is therefore untenable.

Introduction of Cāturmāsya sacrifice by Thibaut for explanation of year-beginning is unjustified.

161. Equinoxes (Viṣuvat) are not mentioned in the *Ṛgveda*, nor are solslices in that Veda. Th. cannot argue validly that non-mention of equinoxes is indicative of want of knowledge of equinoxes on the part of the ancient Indo-Aryans. For this reason, Th. takes to Cāturmāsya sacrifice for an explanation of year-beginning in ancient times. But as J. has pointed out, this explanation is without any basis. The Cāturmāsya sacrifice is a combination of 3 sacrifices, each 4 months long.[2] It has already been shown that J. believes that three different kinds of years—Varṣā, Śarad and Himā—were prevalent in Vedic India, but these had nothing to do with the Cāturmāsya system which probably orginated, according to J., in a later period.

162. The above observations, regarding Cāturmāsya etc., were

1 See para 101.

2 See para 102.

necessary, says Th., for a proper understanding of the passages quoted from the *Taitt.-Saṃ.* and *Tāṇḍya-Br.* bearing on the commencement of Gavām-ayana.

Thibaut believes that his observations re. Cāturmāsya were necessary for a proper assessment of different dates for commencing Gavām-ayana.

Th. interprets the mention, one after another, of four different dates for the said purpose in the two Vedic treatises as tantamount to the rejection of the first three dates and acceptance of the last.

The considerations that weighed with Th. in determining the commencement of the Cāturmāsya sacrifice which he equated with the commencement of the year are now applied by him to the commencement of Gavām-ayana. He finds that the last-mentioned date for Gavām-ayana, viz., that Phālguna or Caitra[1] tallies with the beginning of the first month of Cāturmāsya sacrifice, and points that out to be near a solstice as has been shown in a previous paragraph, the date being apart by about a month and half in case of Phālguna and by about two months and half in case of Caitra. About one more month has to be added if Caitra full-moon mentioned in the *Taitt.-Saṃ.* and *Tāṇḍya-Br.* denotes the 7th of March. But here again there is a difficulty which lies in the fact that the lunar year (=354 days) is shorter than the solar year (=366 days) by 12 days. So if the Phālguna full-moon falls on the 7th February of a year, it will come 12 days earlier the next year, 24 days earlier the following year, and so on. Thus a position arises when no other alternative is left than to admit that the harmony between the lunar and solar year has to be maintained by intercalation of a month every two and a half lunar years.

Thibaut falsely thinks that the ancient Indo-Aryans placed Kṛttikās at the head of the Nakṣatras at equinox, under the influence of Greek astronomy.

163. Though Th. admits that equinox as well as solstice is not mentioned in the *Ṛgveda*, yet he says that no one should be misled to think that Vedic year started from equinox instead of from solstice. His assertion is that ancient Indo-Aryans placed Kṛttikās at the head of the Nakṣatras at equinox in imitation of Greek astronomy. He however adduces no evidence in support of this contention, which cannot be accepted.

1 He has in mind '4 days before the full-moon' which is interpreted as 4 days before the full-moon of Caitra, whereas T. takes it as 4 days before the full-moon of Māgha.

As the lunar months are concerned with tithis, Phālguna Pūrṇamāsaḥ may denote the first day of Phālguna or last day of same which may be in the beginning of Caitra.

A wrong interpretation of Viṣuvat leads Thibaut to reject Tilak's view of same.

164. In regard to Viṣuvat, Th. simply takes it to be the central day of Gavāam-ayana, meaning thereby that it may be any one day of the year with 180 days on either side. He is opposed to T.'s view that Viṣuvat indicated either of the equinoxes six months apart when day and night were equal, as marking year-beginning, without adducing adequate evidence.

As already pointed out before, T. in his description of the component parts of Gavām-ayana, in accordance with the rules laid down in the *Brāhmaṇas*, shows that Viṣuvat would be attached to no other day than the one in which day portion is equal to night portion.

In view of the above consideration, Th.'s contention that T.'s interpretation of Viṣuvat is not supported by any authoritative texts falls to the ground.

Thibaut does not rule out the possibility of Kṛttikās 'marking' the vernal equinox in 2300 B. C.

165. A close examination of Th.'s arguments shows that he could not feel certain about the soundness of his opposition to the antiquity of the Vedas. He admits the possibility of Kṛttikās' coincidence with vernal equinox in 2300 B.C.,[1] when according to Th. an astronomical view different from that in the Brāhmaṇa period prevailed. He allows equinoctial beginning of the year in 2300 B.C., refusing the same in 1100 B.C. Th. states however that the *Taitt.-Saṃ.*, which contains several references to the Kṛttikās as the head of the Kṛttikā-series, cannot be taken to go as far as 2300 B.C., but should be placed about 1100 B.C., without assigning any reason.

The dates of the *Taitt-Saṃ.*, *Tāṇḍya-Br.* and *Kauṣ-Br.* have been inferred from the *Jyotiṣa-Vedāṅga.*

166. It has been pointed out in para 158 that after comparing the *Kauṣ-Br.* with the *Jyotiṣa-Vedāṅga*, Th. thinks that as both the treatises speak of a year-beginning just after amāvasyā, those treatises should be taken as belonging to the same period. He also states that the *Taitt-Saṃ.* and *Tāṇḍya-Br.* belong almost to the same time. He however gives no reason for his inference.

Next he tries to reconcile the time for year-beginning as given in the *Taitt.-Saṃ.* and *Tāṇḍya-Br.* (viz. Ekāṣṭakā, full moon of Phālguna or Caitra, 4 days before the full moon) with that found in the *Kauṣ-Br.* and *Jyotiṣa-Vedāṅga* (viz. the day after new

1 See para 112 where the passage from the *IA.*, 1890, containing Th.'s opinion has been quoted.

moon or amāvasyā in Pauṣa, or Caitra). But he assigns no reason for such reconciliation and states in his conclusion that as the *Jyotiṣa-Vedāṅga* clearly refers to winter solstice taking place in Śraviṣṭhā, it must be the 12th century B.C. in which the event happened. He does not explain why he chooses Śraviṣṭhā instead of Puṣyā, and why the same date could be attributed to the *Taitt.-Saṃ.* and *Kauṣ-Br.*

The attempt made by Thibaut to prove that the ancient Indo-Aryans were lacking in power of observation is futile.

167. Th. agrees with T.'s view in the *Orion* (Chapt. III) that the ancient Indo-Aryans after laborious and prolonged observation determined the motion of the sun and the moon with reference to the 27 Nakṣatras. It is not easy to understand how, after this admission, Th. can state that there was a most confusing mixing up of constellations and divison of the ecliptic.[1] His remark that the Hindus were well-versed in 'arithmetical calculation' loses its force by his denial of their power of accurate observation, for if the observation had been faulty, all calculations based on same would be necessarily incorrect. Th. himself admits that from very early times the Hindus were capable of devising a subdivision of the sun's and moon's path into 27 equal parts and of calculating correctly the places occupied in those parts by the two heavenly bodies.[2] Arithmetical calculation alone without the help of minute observation is not sufficient to enable the Hindus find out the place of the sun and the moon on the ecliptic, or intercalate the year to convert it into luni-solar, or correct the mistake of $\frac{3}{4}$ day in each year after every 40 years.[3]

Insufficient record of astronomical findings by ancient Indo-Aryans does not prove absence of workable knowledge of astronomy.

168. Th. makes a categorical statement that 'no body disputes that observation was never a strong point of Hindu' astronomers. Not a single authority however is quoted by him as evidence Th. is a opinion that early Indo-Aryans did not appreciate the importance of systematic observation. That is why, states Th., they left no direct record of what they did or of the corrections made by them. This argument of Th., however, is based on weak grounds. For records might be lost, or destroyed by climatic and other natural causes, foreign invasions, fires, white ants, other pests, etc. Even

1 See para 114.
2 See para 115.
3 See para 31.

so, non-recording of happenings in itself does not constitute ignorance about them. Had Ṛgvedic literature been completetely silent about their astronomical findings, even then it could not be said that there were none. It is however not a fact that the *Ṛgveda* is silent on astronomical matters. It contains records of observation, implicitly or explicitly, regarding for instance length of the year, and the corrections made.

Thibaut wrongly infers that the ancient Indo-Aryans were unable to measure the proper length of the year.

169. Th. does not keep to his first statement that the ancient Indo-Aryans observed the solstice rightly and counted the year-beginning from there. He modifies it by adding that these observations were corrected only after the composition of the *Siddhāntas*, the product of Greek contact according to him. Th. states that had the ancient Indo-Aryans continued to make correct observations and for a number of years before this, they would have surely gained a proper notion of the length of the year. As it is they never had a right notion.

The repeated mention of a year of 360 days in the *Ṛgveda* does not escape the notice of Th. Nor is he deluded to think that that was all the astronomical knowledge that the ancient Indo-Aryans possessed. He also finds that a year of 366 days was known to the *Jyotiṣa-Vedāṅga*, Garga, etc. His great regret is that these early astronomers never discovered the real length of the year, viz. $365\frac{1}{4}$ days approximately. Th. has to take note that the *Ṛgveda* itself mentions a 13th month or the 7th season, which inevitably proves knowledge of ancient Indo-Aryans about intercalation. So he has to admit that they knew of solar year, but they did not know how to correct the small mistakes in it. A little reflection will show that Th. is mistaken. In paras 25 and 31 above it has been demonstrated that the ancient Indo-Aryans did know to convert the lunar year into luni-solar year, and that they actually corrected the error of $\frac{3}{4}$ day in each year after 40 years.

Th. cannot altogether deny that the ancient Indo-Aryans correctd mistakes in their reckoning of a year. But he finds only 'violent corrections', as distinguished from methodical and continued corrections which were not expected of a people who were incapable of following up a continual and minute observation of the heavens. Here, a pre-conceived notion about the inferiority of ancient Indo-Aryans in matters of astronomy takes hold of Th. and vitiates his arguments.

170. Th. speaks of advanced astronomical knowledge in the *Kauṣ.-Br.* as compared to what is contained in the *Taitt.-Saṃ.* and *Tāṇḍya-Br.* He does not see that this contradicts his previous statement, viz. that all the three books—the *Taitt.-Saṃ. Tāṇḍya-Br.* and the *Kauṣ.-Br.*—are contemporaneous Th. maintains that the *Kauṣ.-Br.* definitely indicates a solstitial beginning of the year. He does not explain how this alone can be taken as an evidence of advanced astronomical knowledge. Admitting, on the one hand, that observation of equinoxes is more difficult and indicates an advanced stage of knowledge, he makes, on the other, a contrary statement to the effect that the *Kauṣ.-Br.*, though speaking of solstital beginning, must be considered to belong to a later and advanced age.

The *Kausītaki-Brāhmaṇa* according to Thibaut contains evidence of advanced astronomical knowledge.

171. Th. relies on Varāhamihira, the famous Hindu astrononomer, one who had made a survey of different Indian systems of astronomy. According to Th., all these systems could be classified into two broad heads: (i) those that were based on Greek astronomy, and (ii) those that were not superior to the *Vedāṅga-Jyotiṣa.* Th. finds that Varāhamihira was familiar with two positions only of the summer solstice,—one in his time and the other recorded in the *Vedāṅga-Jyotiṣa.* From this he concludes that the long interval of 1700 years between the two observations does not speak well of the skill of the Indo-Aryans, and he is led to believe that observations were not made satisfactorily in those times.[1] Apparently, the reason why Th. attaches importance to Varāhamihira is that he has in mind that Varāhamihira flourished in 600 A.D., and the 1700 years antecedent to that date take us to 1100 B.C., the time of origin of the *Taittirīya-Saṃhitā, Tāṇḍya-Brāhmaṇa,* and *Kauṣītaki-Brāhmaṇa,* according to him.

Thibaut refers to Varāhamihira to prove Greek influence on ancient Indo-Aryan astronomy and late date of the *Taitt.-Saṃ.*

172. T. had already alluded to Varāhamihira in his *Orion,*[2] where he states that at the time of Varāhamihira, the vernal equinox coincided with the end of Revatī, the summer solstice being in Punarvasu, and that Varāhmihira distinctly refers, in two places, of his treatise, to the position of the solstices recorded by writers who preceded him:

Varāhamihira's work points to equinoctial beginning of the year, according to Tilak.

1 See para 117.

2 See *The Orion*, pp. 35 ff.

17

आश्लेषार्धादासीद्यदा निवृत्तिः किलोष्णकिरणस्य ।

युक्तमयनं तदासीत् सांप्रतमयनं पुनर्वसुतः ॥[1]

When the return of the sun took place from the middle of Aśleṣā, it was then *rightly* the tropic. It now takes place from Punarvasu.—Varāhamihira, *Pañca-Siddhāntikā*[2]

In the *Bṛhatsaṃhitā*, III. 1 and 2, Varāhamihira mentions the same older position cf the solstitial points.[3]

अश्लेषार्धाद्दक्षिणमुत्तरमयनं रवेर्धनिष्ठाद्यम् ।

नूनं कदाचिदासीद्येनोक्तं पूर्वशास्त्रेषु ॥

साम्प्रतमयनं सवितुः कर्कटकाद्यं मृगादितश्चान्यं ।

उक्ताभावो विकृतिः प्रत्यक्षपरीक्षणै र्व्यक्तिः ॥[4]

From the middle of Aśleṣā, the solstices (why not equinoxes?) began, Dhaniṣṭhā today takes place from the sun. What has been stated in the former Śāstras is not less. Now at Karkaṭaka from the sun and at Mṛga from another are the solstices. Let the readers ascertain for themselves by actual observation which of the two positions of the solstices is the correct one, whether the older position of the solstices or that given by the writer.

It is concluded by T. that at the time of Varāhamihira there existed works that placed the winter solstice in the beginning of (divisional) Dhaniṣṭhā and the summer solstice in the middle of Aśleṣā. The above is corroborated by quotations from Garga and Parāśara. It appears that the system of commencing the year with the month of Māgha was once actually a custom. It corresponded with the above positions of the solstices. Amarasiṃha (1. 4. 13), Suśruta (I. 6) and Vāgbhatta (III. 2), and the Mahābhārata (Anuśāsanaparva, 167, 26-28) indicate that "winter solstice must have coincided in those days with the beginning of Dhaniṣṭhā as described in *Vedāṅga-Jyotiṣa*."[5]

Winter solstice at the beginning of Dhaniṣṭhā is indicative of year-beginning in Māgha.

173. T. considers the *Vedāṅga-Jyotiṣa* to be a reliable and

1 See Colebrooke's *Essays*, vol. II. p. 387. The verse may now be found in Thibaut's edition of the work.—Tilak, *The Orion*, p. 35 fn.

2 Tilak, *The Orion*, p. 35

3 *Ibid.*, p. 35.

4 *Ibid.*, p. 36 fn.

5 *Ibid.*, pp. 36-37

authoritative treatise on astronomy.[1] It gives the following positions of solstices and equinoxes:

Tilak on the *Vedāṅga-Jyotiṣa.*

1. The winter solstice in the beginning of Śraviṣṭhā.
2. The vernal equinox in 10° of Bharaṇī.
3. The summer solstice in the middle of Aśleṣā.
4. The autumnal equinox in 3°20′ of Viśākhā.

From the above data, modern astronomers have been able to calculate, according to T., that the solstitial colure occupied the position mentioned above between 1269 B.C. and 1181 B.C., according as the rate of precession is 50″ or 48·6" a year.[2]

The question whether the above records are results of observation or are mere traditions is superfluous to T., for he is satisfied that ample confirmatory evidence is found in the Vedic works which must be dated much earlier than the *Vedāṅga-Jyotiṣa.*[3]

1 Tilak's remarks re. *Vedāṅga-Jyotiṣa* are worth quoting. "We need not, therefore, have any doubts about the authencity of a work which describes this older system and gives rules of preparing a calendar accordingly. Now this is what the *Vedāṅga-Jyotiṣa* has done. It is a small treatise on Vedic calendar, and though some of its verses still remain unintelligible, yet we now know enough of the work to ascertain the nature of the calculations given therein."—*The Orion*, p. 37

2 *Ibid.*, p. 38

3 *Ibid.*, p. 39

174. A summary of position according to *Taitt.-Saṃ.*, *Tāṇḍya-Br.* and *Kauṣ.-Br.* is given below:

The essential proposition according to the 3 treatises.	According to the *Taittirīya-Saṃhitā* and *Tāṇḍya-Brāhmaṇa*	According to the *Kauṣītaki-Brāhmaṇa*
	Year-beginning	Year-beginning
	I. Ekāṣṭakā, consecration on; wife of the year. Disadvantages: (i) distress, (for it is very cold on the 8th day of the dark half of Māgha); (ii) last season, (for the month of Māgha belongs to the last season); (iii) reversed period (for the year ends with Māgha and begins in Māgha in a reversed way, the beginning and end falling in the same month). Therefore rejected.	I. Taiṣa (Pauṣa) Pratipad (Śukla).
	II. Phalgunī fullmoon, Disadvantage: (i) Viṣuvat in Bhādrapada, therefore in rains.	II. Māgha Pratipad (Śukla).
	III. Citrā fullmoon,	III. Caitra Pratipad (Śukla)
	IV. 4 days before full-moon (may be Māgha or Caitra).	

175. If we now look at the two different sorts of passages already quoted, the following points among others strike us at once.

Comparison between the *Taitt.-Sam.* and the *Kauṣ.-Br.*

I. Following up of the sun's course during the performance of the Gavām-ayana is the most important thing in the *Kauṣ.-Br.* It overshadows all other considerations. In the *Taitt.-Saṃ.* (and *Tāṇḍya.-Br.*), the sun's course is not described at all, its main object being to choose the most suitable date for beginning the Sattra and therefore the year. It is true that in both sets the advantages and disadvantages of the different dates are discussed and weighed, but the sun's course is indicated in the *Kauṣ.-Brāhmaṇa* alone.

The sun's course is the point of discussion in the *Kauṣ.-Br.*

II. The directions for commencing the sacrifices are much simpler in the *Kauṣītakh Brāhmaṇa* than in the other two. It prescribes the same date, viz., the day after the amāvasyā in the months of Pauṣa, Māgha and Caitra. In the case of the other two works, two more dates are prescribed in addition to the two fullmoons of Phālguna and Caitra, viz. the 8th day of the dark half of Māgha (Ekāṣṭakā) and 4 days before the full moon (of Māgha or Caitra).

Directions regarding the beginning of the sacrifices are simpler in the *Kauṣ.-Br.*

III. Of the months mentioned by these treatises for the commencement of the sacrifice, the *Taitt.-Saṃ.* omits Pauṣa and the *Kauṣ.-Br.* Phālguna. But both the sets are of one opinion in regard to Caitra being the most suitable —but not in regard to the particular time of that month. The *Taitt.-Saṃ.* prefers *Pūrṇimā,* and the *Kauṣ.-Br.* Śukla Pratipad or a date 15 days afterwards. The omission of Pauṣa in the *Taitt.-Saṃ.* can be explained as due to the work having been composed before year-beginning in Pauṣa commenced at a later time. It only shows that the *Kaus.-Br.* was composed at a time much later than the *Taitt.-Saṃ.* But it is however difficult to explain the omission of Phālguna in the *Kauṣ.-Br.* as that month has been repeatedly referred to as suitable by the *Taitt.-Saṃ.* and other *Brāhmaṇas.*

The selection of months of sacrifice by she works.

IV. In contrast to the *Taitt. Saṃ.* (and the *Tāṇḍya-Br.*), the *Kauṣ. Br.* directly mentions the 13th month, thereby indicating

The pointed mention of the 13th month by the *Kauṣ.-Br.*

that the subject-matter of its special study was the intercalated year and framing of rules for performance of Gavām-ayana in that year. These rules must necessarily be different from those that were general. Th. noticed the fact, but not its full significance.

176. In the first chapter of the *Kauṣ.-Br.*, from which the passage has been quoted occurs the following:

पौर्णमासं प्रथमायै तन्त्रं भवत्यामावस्यां द्वितीयायै तेन हास्य दर्शपूर्णमासावरजौ ...भवतः यज्ञस्यैव समृद्धै द्वादश दद्द्यादश वै मासाः संवत्सरः संवत्सरस्यैनाऽप्त्या अश्वं ददाति यत्त्रयोदशो मास स्तस्याप्त्यै ॥ I. 1

The meaning of full moon and new moon offering.

[The full moon offering is the model of the first (sacrifice) the new moon offering of the second;[1] thereby does he commence the new...and full moon (offerings). (So they serve) for the perfection of the sacrifice. Twelve (cows) should he give; the year has twelve months; verily (they serve) to make up the year. He gives a horse as thirteenth to make up the thirteenth month.[2]]

Thus, there were two principal days for offerings at the sacrifice:

(1) one at the full moon;

and, (2) one at the new moon.

It is needless to point out that both the offerings could not be made at one and the same sacrifice. The full moon offering should be taken as the model or general rule for Gavām-ayana, where no 13th month is necessary; and the new moon offering is but the one in an intercalated year with a 13th month, and the *Kauṣ.-Br.* deals with the same.

This is corroborated by the next passage (quoted) of the *Kauṣ.-Br.* which says—

त एतं त्रयोदशमधिचरं मासमुपयन्त्येताबान् बै संबतसरो यदेष त्रयोदश मासस्तत्रैव सर्वः संवत्सर आप्तो भवति ॥ XIX. 2

1 Two sorts of sacrifice, presumably one for ordinary and another for intercalated year, are indicated here.

2 Keith, *Rigveda Brāhmaṇas*, pp. 347-348

3 तावान्वै means in reality 'to that extent.'

[They obtain this thirteenth additional month; the year is as this thirteenth month; in it verily whole year is obtained.[1]]

त्रयोदशं वा एतं मासमाप्नुवन्ति यद्विश्वजितमुपयन्त्येतावान् वै संबत्सरो यदेष त्रयोदशो मासस्तदत्रैव सर्वः संवत्सर आप्तो भवति तमाहुरेकाहः षडह इति। XXV. 11

[They obtain this thirteenth month in that they perform the Viśvajit; the thirteenth month is as great as the year; here verily the whole year is made up. Of it they say 'the six day (rite) is one day rite.'][2]

The *Kauṣ-Br.* gives above a hint as to how the 13th month is obtained. It points out that Viśvajit in the Sattra, though one day rite, is to be considered here as a six day rite. 24 more days are necessary for making a full month. These are to be added to the very beginning of the Sattra, 12 days for Dīkṣā and 12 days for Upasads, as T. has indicated at the time of his treatment of Ekāṣṭakā.[3] In this way a full month is left out for intercalation.

The *Kauṣ-Br.* deals with sacrifices in intercalated years of a time 1000 years later than the *Taitt-Saṃ*.

177. Phālguna as well as Caitra full moon is mentioned by the *Taitt.-Saṃ.* as the mouth i.e. the beginning of the year. Therefore, if the purpose of the *Kauṣ-Br.* be treatment of intercalated years, the first month should be in Māgha or Phālguna full moons. But the *Kauṣ-Br.* instead gives the dates as Śukla Pratipad of Pauṣa or Māgha and Caitra.

There is no reason to think that the dates are arbitrarily fixed by the *Kauṣ.-Br.* They are as valid as those given by the *Taitt.-Saṃ.* Therefore there must be sufficient reason for the discrepancy. It has already been pointed out[4] that a change from one Nakṣatra epoch to another indicated the passing away of 2000 years more or less, and recession of a month. Therefore the recession of 15 days should be taken as passing away of 1000 years and the middle of a Nakṣatra epoch. A thousand years back from the full moon of Māgha or Phālguna is in reality Śulka Pradipad of Pauṣa or Māgha, to which is added Śukla Pratipad of Caitra. Thus the *Kauṣ.-Br.* gives dates for sacrifice for intercalated years, later than those given in the *Taitt--Saṃ*, by 1000 years.

The *Kauṣ.-Br.* states that there was a preference for the month of Pauṣa for commencing the Gavām-ayana. The *Taitt.-Saṃ.*

1 Keith., *Rigveda Brāhmanas*, p. 452 2 *Ibid.*, p. 493

3 Tilak, *The Orion*, p. 51: "The first twelve days of a *sattra* are taken up in consecration and twelve more in *upasads* after which the regular *sattra* sacrifice commences." 4 See para 142,

and *Tāṇḍya-Br.* speak of no such preference. The conclusion therefore becomes irresistible that the *Kauṣ.-Br.* is of a much later origin inasmuch as the month of Pauṣa indicates a year-beginning in a later Nakṣatra epoch. This preference for Pauṣa together with the next statement that 'they (thus) obtain the additional thirteenth (month)' indicates that the month of Pauṣa should be taken as the intercalary month, being reserved for some preliminary rites. Therefore, the real beginning of the year must be understood to be in Māgha. That is why the sun is said to rest on the new moon day of Māgha, but not of Pauṣa or Caitra. The Caitra beginning of the year, indicating an occurrence in a remote Nakṣatra epoch, stands by itself, and is not put together with Vaiśākha as alternative, perhaps because at that time 12 days, and not a month, were added to each year to convert it into a luni-solar one.

The indirect reference to intercalation by the *Taitt.-Saṃ.*

178. The *Taitt.-Saṃ.* and the *Tāṇḍya-Br.* refer also to the performance of the Sattra in intercalated years, but not directly like the *Kauṣ.-Br.* These two works speak of Phālguna and Caitra full moons as the mouth of the year, but not of Ekāṣṭakā or 4 days before the full moon as the mouth.

For convenience of reference, the English rendering of the portions that refer to 'Ekāṣṭakā' (at the beginning) and '4 days before the full moon' (at the end) are joined together and reproduced below:

"Those who are about to conscerate themselves for the year (sacrifice) should do so on the Ekāṣṭakā (day). The Ekāṣṭakā is the wife of the year; and he [i.e. the year] lives in her [i.e. the Ekāṣṭakā] for that night. (Therefore they) practically sacrifice (by) beginning the year. Those that sacrifice on the Ekāṣṭakā, sacrifice to the distressed (period) of the year. It is the season (*dual*) whose name comes last.

"They should consecrate themselves for the sacrifice four days before the full moon. Their Kraya [i.e. the purchase of Soma] falls on the Ekāṣṭakā. Thereby they do not render the Ekāṣṭakā void [i.e. of no consequence]. Their Sutyā [i.e. the extraction of Soma juice] falls in the first [i.e. the bright] half (of the month). Their months [i.e. monthly sacrifices] fall on the first half".[1]

1 See para 61

Normally, the *Taitt.-Saṃ.* is expected to place the beginning of the year in Pūrṇimā. Hence selection of the 8th day of the dark half of Māgha (and not the full moon of Māgha) is a deviation that requires explanation. All that is suggested in this portion is that the Ekāṣṭakā is the wife of the Year, who lives (or lingers as it were) in her that night. This is the longest night of the year and therefore the text indicates a year-beginning in winter solstice. There is no doubt that the general rule was that the year was to commence in Māghī full moon. The beginning of the year 7 days afterwards is indicative of a recession of about 500 years;[1] in other words, the year-beginning in Māghī full moon is equivalent to commencement of the Kṛttikā epoch, and the Ekāṣṭakā, as beginning of the year, occurred 500 years afterwards.

The *Taitt.-Saṃ.* does not however stop here. It enjoins the commencement of the sacrifice 4 days before the full moon of Māgha. Adding together these 4 days before the full moon and 8 days after the full moon of Māgha (Ekāṣṭakā), 12 days are obtained. These 12 days are then left out, presumably because they are intercalated from each year which begins properly after these 12 days.[2] This was before a full month was intercalated. Thus the *Taitt.-Saṃ.* and *Tāṇḍya-Br.* contain hints not only for intercalation but also for calculation of other dates during the prevalence of a Nakṣatra epoch.

Tilak is justified in holding that the year commenced in equinox in Vedic India.

179. It may now be concluded that Th.'s assertion that the *Taitt.-Saṃ*, *Tāṇḍya-Br.* and *Kauṣ.-Br.* belong to the same period has been proved to be untenable. Further, his view that T. would have reached a different conclusion if he had taken notice of the passage of the *Kauṣ.-Br.* is mistaken. This *Brāhmaṇa* contains no evidence that the *Jyotiṣa-Vedāṅga* belonged to the same period as the said *Brāhmaṇa*. Sufficient has been indicated

1 The Kṛttikā epoch was nearly 2000 years long [see para 142]. It has been pointed out by T. that Aśvinī and Pauṣa, Kṛttikā and Māgha, and Mṛgaśiras and Phālguna, are pairs of successive year-beginnings, depending consecutively on the precession of the equinoxes [*The orion*, p. 200]. So there is a recession of a month before the lapse of the epoch. Accordingly, a recession of 7 days or ¼ th of a month indicates 500 years after the epoch.

2 "The sacrificial literature of India still preserves the memory of these days by ordaining that a person wishing to perform a yearly sacrifice should devote 12 days (dvādashāha) before its commencement to the preparatory rites."—Tilak, *The Orion*, p. 16

above regarding the gap of the time between the different dates of year-beginning in the *Taitt.-Saṃ.* itself, and that between the *Taitt.-Saṃ.* and *Kauṣ.-Br.*

T.'s inference that year commenced in equinox in Vedic times is proved by the very nature of the Sattra itself. For, an analysis of its component parts has shown that Gavām-ayana began in Viśuvat, i. e. the equinoctial point. Th. blundered in thinking that all the different dates mentioned by the *Taitt.-Saṃ.*, the *Tāṇḍya-Br.* and the *Kauṣ.-Br* one after another, prevailed at one and the same period, and their non-acceptence later was due to inconveniences for the performance of the rituals on particular dates. In reality, all the three treatises speak of different Nakṣatra epochs, clearly denoted by the different months—Pauṣa, Māgha, Phālguna and Caitra standing for Aśvinī, Kṛttikā, Mṛgaśiras and Punarvasu epochs respectively.

C. An Examination of Bühler's Statements

Bühler is satisfied that the main propositions of Jacobi and Tilak have been established.

180. B. is convinced by the arguments of J. and T. that the ancient Indo-Aryans were familiar not only with the Kṛttikā-series but also with the Mṛgaśiras-series, and that Mṛgaśiras in a much earlier time coincided with the vernal equinox as the Kṛttikās did in the later epoch. B. does not claim any mathematical preciseness for the theory of the two scholars, but he thinks that evidences adduced by them are so strong and cogent that no doubt is left about the possibility of the assumptions. Their discovery of a new foundation for Vedic chronology gives much satisfaction to B.

Bühler's explanation of year-beginning at different dates.

181. B. holds the view that in a vast country like India, the possibility of different reckonings of the year from different places at the same time should not be ruled out. To him however the question of year-beginning is of less importance than that of finding out the particular Nakṣatras through which the sets of colures passed, because that alone determined the antiquity or otherwise of the time mentioned. According to B., the latter question has been satisfactorily solved by J. and T.

While not denying the importance of the second problem, one cannot overlook the fact that year-beginning on different dates is a sure pointer to a definite period of a particular Nakṣatra epoch.

182. B. fixes the beginning of the Mṛgaśiras epoch at about 3800 B.C. J.'s Table shows the date to be 4420 B.C. B. substracts more than 600 years from that figure in consideration of the mistake that might have crept into the calculations of the early astronomers. But this mistake might as well have taken place in the opposite direction. Thus according to B. the lower limit of Mṛgaśiras epoch is 3800 B.C. and the upper limit accepted by T. is about 5000 B.C.

Bühler's fixation of the time of Mṛgaśiras epoch at 3800 B. C. gives the lower limit.

183 B. has not the least doubt in his mind that the Kṛttikā-series was completely an Indian invention. Copious mentions of Kṛttikās at the head of Nakṣatras in different Vedic texts convince him about the same. But B. is not so sure about Mṛgaśiras-series. He is rather inclined to the view that this series was borrowed from other nations.

Bühler's view that Mṛgaśiras-series was of foreign origin is untenable.

As the *Brāhmaṇas* do not give the list of Nakṣatras anywhere with Mṛgaśiras at their head, B. might have been erroneously led to the conclusion that Mṛgaśiras-series was of foreign origin. The particular reason for placing Kṛttikās at the head of Nakṣatras might be due to the fact that the *Taitt.-Sam.* etc. were composed during the prevalence of that Nakṣatra epoch. This does not mean that the ancient Indo-Aryans were ignorant of the older Mṛgaśiras-series. On the other hand, the *Ṛgveda* contains, as has been repeatedly shown, abundant references to the equinoctial year-beginning in the Mṛgaśiras epoch, which points to the existence once of a Nakṣatra-series with Mṛgaśiras at the head. No evidence has been cited by B. for his inference that the Mṛgaśiras-series was of foreign origin.

D. Winternitz's view

184. Winternitz has also discussed in his *History of Indian Literature*, vol. 1, pp, 190 ff (1908) the problem of the age of the Veda, and has made certain observations which should be examined here.

Winternitz wants to fix 1100 B. C. or thereabout as the time when Vedic literature commenced.

Winternitz weighs some of the literary and astronomical statements of scholars to find out which of them may be acceptable. His references are to Friedrich Schlegel who expects from India nothing less than "enlightenment upon the history of the primitive world, so dark until now;" to A. Weher who in 1852 wrote in his *History of Indian Literature* that "the literature of India passes generally for the most ancient literature of which we possess written records, and justly so;" and to Max Müller, who was first to attempt a reconstruction of chronology of the oldest Indian literature." Winternitz also mentions some of the pioneers who depended on astronomical data for establishing the chronology of the oldest Indian literature, such as Ludwig who based his conclusions on the eclipses of the sun; Jacobi and Tilak who state that at the period of the *Brāhmaṇas,* the Pleiades (Kṛttikās), the starting point of the Nakṣatra series, at the time coincided with the vernal equinox. In the Vedic texts, however, there are traces of an older calendar in which vernal equinox fell in Orion (Mṛgaśiras), while Jacobi alone speaks of the text referring to the antiquity of the Pole Star. Winternitz does not rule out the possibility of ancient Indian literature being dated 2000 or 2500 B. C., in consideration of the evidences found there. But he does not think that astronomy can be of help in this regard. On the other hand, he holds that attempts to determine the period of the Veda with the aid of astronomy have come to grief. Therefore, his advice is to steer clear of any fixed dates.

If however he had followed his own advice, he would not have tried to fix the date of Vedic literature at about 1100 B. C. He rejects not only all the astronomical findings of the scholars, but also literary evidences regarding the high antiquity of the Vedas. He forgets that astronomy may be as good an aid as literature for determining the age of the *Ṛgveda.*

(6) THE POLE STAR

1. *Jacobi*

The determination of time with the help of the Pole Star.

185. Two results followed, according to J., from the precession of the equinox, viz.,

(1) There was an alteration of the colures;

(2) "along with the gradual alteration of the celestial equator its north (and south) pole continued to move in a circle of 23½[1] semi-diameter in a period of about 26000 years round the fixed poles of the ecliptic. In this way, one star after another is drawn nearer the north pole and becomes the *north or Pole Star.*"[2]

1 23½°

2 *I. A.*, 1894, p. 157

J. distinguishes the Pole Star from the North Star thus: the bright star standing nearest the pole at any time is called the North Star; and the star whose distance from the pole is so slight that for all practical purposes, it may be called fixed (Dhruva) is the Pole Star.

The following table of North stars from 5000 B. C. till 2000 A. D. was prepared by J.

Name of the Star	Magnitude	Polar Distance	Year
ι Draconis	3.0	4° 38'	4,700 B.C.
α do	3.3	0° 6'	2,780 B.C.
κ do	3.3	4° 44'	1,290 B.C.
β Ursae Minoris (Little Bear)	2.0	6° 22'	1,060 B.C.
α do	2.0	0° 28'	2,100 A.D.

Only two stars of the above can, according to J., be called Pole Stars, viz. α Draconis and α Ursae Minoris. The rest spin round a circle and could be easily observed. J.'s statement that it was only the Gṛhya Sūtras which first mention the Pole Star as having a place in the Hindu ritual of marriage, and that it was a custom in vogue much anterior to the time of the Gṛhya Sūtras,[1] can be properly comprehended only when the dates given above are borne in mind. The North Star which was in reality a Pole Star for a long time (about 2780 B.C. to 1500 B.C.) must have been, states J., none other than α Draconis.[2]

As α Draconis remained Dhruva during several centuries before and after 2800 B.C., the Sūtra must be referring to the Vedic period, states J.

2. *Whitney*

Whitney attaches no importance to Pole Star.

186. W. however sets no value by the above argument of J. He calls this a supporting evidence and cannot attribute to it greater value. "The mention of a polar star (dhruva, lit. 'fixed') by the Gṛihya-Sūtras, solely and alone as something which a bride is to be taken out and made to look at on the evening of her wedding-day" does not prove J.'s thesis, according to W. Considering who the observers

1 The Sūtras seem to refer to Vedic period and the date conforms to the date derivable from the position of the colures.—See J.s' article in *I. A* , 1894, pp. 157, 158

2 Alcor-Arundhatī stands near Ursae Majoris and is shown to the bride. *I. A.*, 1894, p. 158

were and for what trifling purpose their observation was used, W. concludes that "any star not too far from the pole would have satisfied both the newly wedded woman and the exhibitor ; there is no need of assuming that the custom is one handed down from the remote period when ≺ Draconis was really very close to the pole, across an interval of two or three thousand years, during which there is no mention of pole-star, either in *Veda* or in *Brāhmaṇa*."[1]

3. *Bühler*

187. B. is of opinion that J. and T. have been able to prove that "some of the Hindu rites and sacrifices existed even before the time when the Kṛittika-series was invented, and were settled long before the year 2000 B.C." He states that the latter inference is supported by J.'s evidences regarding the connection of the Dhruva Nakṣatra or Pole Star with the ancient Vedic marriage ritual, a connection known through the Gṛhya-Sūtras but dating from very remote past.

Bühler states that the Hindu rite of showing the Pole Star at marriage ritual is as old as the Veda.

B. admits on J.'s showing that there existed a real Pole Star for about 600 years (3100 B.C. to 2500 B.C.), and that during these years, the husband used to point it out to his bride and exhort her never to forsake her home, just as the star never changed its position.

B. states that J. might have added, that "in later times, even during the Vedic period, the motion of the pole-star had been observed by the Hindus. In the *Maitrāyaṇa-Brāhmaṇa Upanishad* the motion of the pole-star is mentioned as one of the many instances of mutability to which all terrestrial and celestial beings are subject."[2]

4. *Winternitz*

188. In discussing the Age of the Veda,[3] Winternitz like B. refers to J. and T. for their opinion on the antiquity of the Vedic literature. Winternitz describes how J. arrived at 4500 B.C. to 2500 B.C. as the period during which Vedic civilisation flourished, and how J. confirms it by "a second astronomical observation," in the following way:

Winternitz does not attach much value to astronomical evidence. He rejects Jacobi's theory about Pole Star.

1 *I. A.*, 1895, p. 365

2 *I.A.*, 1894, p. 245 (S. B. E., XV. includes this Upaniṣad,

3 M. Winternitz, A *History of Indian Literature*, vol. 1, (1927). pp. 290-310

'The Gṛhyasūtras tell us of a marriage-custom in ancient India, according to which the bride and bridegroom, after they had arrived at their new home, had to sit silently on the hide of a bull, till the stars became visible, whereupon the bridegroom showed his bride the *Pole star*, called *dhruva*, "the constant one", and at the same time uttered a prayer, as for example, "Be constant, prospering in my house," whereto she replied: "Constant art thou, may I be constant in the house of my husband." This marriage-custom in which a "constant star" figures as the symbol of unchangeable constancy, must have originated at a time in which a brighter star stood so near the celestial pole that it seemed, to the observers of that time, to be standing still. Now it is again a result of the precession that, with the gradual alteration of the celestial equator, its North Pole also moves away, describing in about 26,000 years a circle of 23½ degrees radius around the constant pole of the ecliptic. By this means one star after another slowly moves towards the North Pole and becomes North Star or Pole Star ; but only from time to time does a *brighter* star approach the Pole so closely, that it can, for all practical purposes, be regarded as "a constant one" (dhruva). At present [1927] Alpha, a star of the second magnitude, in the Little Bear, is the Pole Star of the Northern hemisphere. This star, of course, cannot be meant when the Pole Star is spoken of in Vedic times, because only 2000 years ago this star was still so far removed from the pole that it could not possibly have been designated as the "constant one". Not until 2780 B.C. do we meet with another Pole Star which merited this name. At that time Alpha Draconis stood so near to the Pole for over 500 years that it must have appeared immovable to those who observed with the naked eye. We must, then, place the origin of the name of Dhruva, as well as the custom of showing the "constant" star to the bride on her marriage evening as the symbol of constancy, into a period in which Alpha Draconis was Pole Star, that is, in the first half of the third millenary B.C."[1]

189. Though in the above passage, Winternitz represents the view of J. very ably, he does not seem to subscribe to the same. He states that the most serious objection has been raised against Kṛttikas being in junction with the vernal equinox in ancient

1 *Ibid.*, pp. 296, 297

Astronomically, Winternitz believes 1100 B.C. to be the date of the Pole Star

times. On the *Śatapatha Brāhmaṇa*,[1] II, 1, 2, 3 depends the above theory. It is, according to Winternitz, wrongly interpreted as Pleiades "do not swerve from the East" i.e. they rose "due east" ("which would have been the case in the third millenary B.C., and would point to a knowledge of the vernal equinox"). He thinks that the correct interpretation should perhaps be that "they remain visible in the eastern region for a considerable time—during several hours—every night, which was the case about 1100 B.C."[2] He states that be cannot rule out the possiblity of one of the lesser stars in the Little Bear having been visible (in 1250 B.C. or later still) as the Pole Star in the clear sky.

Winternitz gives credit to Prey of Prague University for finding out that in "about 1100 B. C. the *Pleiades* rose approximately 13° to the north of the easl point, approaching nearer and nearer the east line, and crossing it as late as 2^h 11^m after their rise, at a height of 29°, when seen from a place situated at 25° North latitude. They thus remain almost due east long enough to serve as a convenient basis for orientation."[3] Winternitz thinks that this interpretation is also supported by Baudhāyana-Śrautasūtra, 27.5, where Pleiades is said not to depart from the eastern region. Winternitz does not deny that "about 2100 B.C. or 3100 B.C., the Pleiades touched the east line earlier, but they proceeded southward so rapidly that they were not suitable for orientation."[4]

1 Sankar B. Dikshit in the *I.A.*, 1895, pp. 245, 246 reproduces the passage.

एकं द्वे त्रीणि चत्वारीति वा अन्यानि नक्षत्राण्यथैता एव भूयिष्ठा यत्कृत्तिकास्त-द्भूमानमेवैतदुपैति तस्मात् कृत्तिकास्वादधीत ॥२॥

एतो ह वै प्राच्यै दिशो न च्यवन्ते सर्वाणि ह वा अन्यानि नक्षत्राणि प्राच्यै दिशश्च्यवन्ते तत् प्राच्यामेवास्यैतद्दिश्याहितौ भवतस्तस्मात् कृत्तिकास्वादधीत ॥३॥

Dikshit's literal translation :

Certainly one, two, three, four: so [are] other *Nakṣatras*, and these only are many, which [are] Kṛttikāḥ: surely [he who consecrates the sacred fires on Kṛttikāḥ] gets that plenty of it ; [one] should, therefore, consecrate [the sacred fires] on Kṛttikāḥ. These, certainly, do not deviate from the eastern direction. All other *nakṣatras* deviate from the eastern direction. His [two sacred fires] become consecrated in the very east. He should, therefore, consecrate [the fires] on Kṛttikāḥ.

Cf. Eggeling's trans. in S.B.E., vol. XII, p. 282

2 Winternitz, *History*, p. 298

3 *Ibid.*, p. 298 fn.

4 *Ibid.*

EXAMINATION OF THE DIFFERENT VIEWPOINTS ON POLE STAR

190. It has already been stated that W. attaches little importance to J.'s theory that a particular star was ever called a pole star and denies that the observation of pole star by the married couple as pointed out by the *Gṛhya-Sūtras* refers to a custom that was prevalent at about 3000 B.C. He holds that any star near to the pole was good enough to be the Pole Star provided it was not much further away. W. refuses to believe that the ancient Indo-Aryans did really have a custom of observing a particular star as Pole Star. According to him any star was good enough to be so shown.[1]

According to Whitney, any star not much further away from Pole, served the purpose of the Pole Star.

It is true that the same star cannot be the pole star throughout the ages, that is to say that the pole star has a motion, however small, and changes its position, so that a new star becomes the pole star, after the lapse of hundreds of years.

191. B. is of opinion that J. has been able to establish the antiquity of the custom of showing the Pole Star to the bride by the bridegroom from Vedic literature.

Bühler supports Jacobi as against Whitney.

Winternitz does not think so. He attacks J.'s point of view from another direction. J. identifies the Pole Star with Alpha Draconis, which was shown, according to him, to the bride by the bridegroom in about 3000 B.C.[2] Winternitz is of opinion that this was not the case, for according to him, J. has not correctly interpreted the *Śātapatha-Brāhmaṇa*, II. 1, 2, 3, on which he bases his theory. Had this interpretation been correctly made, the time (i.e. 3000 B.C.) referred to by J. could have been accepted. J.'s whole theory falls through, according to Winternitz, due to his incorrect interpretation of the passage. Winternitz interpretes the passage to mean "they remain visihle in the eastern region for a considerable time" and finds with the help of his astronomer that the event was possible only in 1100 B.C.

192. By the passage quoted in the footnote of para 189 Dikshit understands that what is meant is that Kṛttikās were always seen due east, while other Nakṣatras were to the right or to the left of this point. "It means that in those days the Kṛttikāḥ

1 Cf. W.'s statement that any month was good enough to begin the year with in Vedic times.

2 See para 187.

were on the equator, or that their declination was nil, when the passage was composed."[1]

On account of the precession of the equinoxes, the place of the Kṛttikās with reference to the equator, is not always the same. "Taking the annual precession of the equinoxes to be 50°, and calculating roughly, I find that Tauri, the brightest star of the Pleiades, was on the equator about 2990 B.C. or, roughly speaking, in 3000 B.C." If the annual precession be less than 50°, the date would be earlier still. Dikshit therefore thinks that as the tense used is the present tense, the Brāhmaṇa or at least this passage was composed about 3000 B.C.[2]

Dikshit is of opinion that 3000 B.C. is the date of the composition of the *Śatapatha-Brāhmaṇa*

193. Rāy supports the interpretation of the passage by Dikshit, and finds no reason to agree with Macdonell and Keith's assertion that the aforesaid passage of the *Śatapatha-Brāhmaṇa* is untrustworthy. Rāy however does not agree with Dikshit, J. and T. that the date of composition of this Brāhmaṇa was 3000 B.C. According to him, the incident referred to might have happened on the date, for Pleiades remained fixed, as it were, in that position for nearly seven or eight hundred years (3300 B.C. to 2500 B.C.), but that does not necessarily indicate that 3000 B.C. was the date of composition of *Ś.-Br.*, It was composed, according to Rāy, within the range of 3300 B.C. and 2500 B.C.[3]

Rāy's interpretation of the passage of the *Śatapatha-Brāhmaṇa.*

194. A question may arise that if the custom of showing the Pole Star to a newly married bride was prevalent in India as long ago as about 3000 B.C., why has not this fact been mentioned anywhere in the Vedas or the Brāhmaṇas? Its mention in the Gṛhya-Sūtras, which were much later compositions indicates, one should think, much later date, as suggested by Winternitz and other scholars.

The non-mention of Pole Star in the Veda and Brāhmaṇa does not vittiate its being known early to the Indo-Aryans.

The only reference to the fixity of a heavenly body is to the fixity of the Pleiades found in the *Śatapatha-Brāhmaṇa.* Rāy points out that for nearly 800 years, Pleiades (Kṛttikā) was observed to rise in the east in the evening for 5½ months every year and that

1 *IA.*, 1895, p. 245

2 *Ibid.*, 1895, The age of the *Śatapatha-Brāhmaṇa,* by Sankar B. Dikshit, pp. 245, 246

3 Jogesh Chandra Rāy, *Veder Devatā O Kṛṣṭikāl* (The gods of the Veda and the age of Vedic culture), 1361 B.S. pp. 43-53

it was natural for the people to take the star to be a fixed one during that period. It is to be presumed that before and after this star, other stars were found on the horizon and appeared fixed. If the *Śatapatha-Brāhmaṇa* speaks of a tradition earlier than 1100 B.C. (an appropriate date according to Winternitz), why should it not also refer, one may pertinently ask, to a tradition prevalent at an earlier date (say 3000 B C. or so), when another star did not swerve from the east i.e. was the fixed star. There is no doubt that this statement of not swerving from the east is correct in reference to all earlier stars as well; and it seems that this cause more than any other was responsible for the selection of a particular star as the *mukham* or beginning of each star-series.

It is remarkable that modern treatises on astronomy also support the above statement. For instance, says Ball: "A complete journey of the Pole occupies the considerable period of about 25,867 years, The drawing shows the position of the Pole at the several dates from 4000 B. C. to 2000 A. D. A glance at this map brings prominently before us how casual is the proximity of the pole to the Pole Star. At present, indeed, the distance of the two is actually lessening, but afterwards the distance will increase until, when half of the revolution has been accomplished, the pole will be at a distance of twice the radius of the circle from the Pole Star, It will then happen that the pole will be near the bright star Vega or *a* Lyrae, so that our successors some 12000 years hence may make use of Vega for many of the purposes for which the Pole Star is at present employed. Looking back into past ages, we see that some 2,000 or 3,000 years B.C. the star α Draconis was suitably placed to serve as Pole Star,"...[1] The non-mention of Pole Star, as such, in the Veda is therefore no valid ground for thinking that it was unknown to the ancient Indo-Aryans.

In astronomical parlance, when the declination of Mṛgaśiras on the equator was nil, Mṛgaśiras was made to head the list of the Nakṣatras. In that case, each of the Nakṣatras that gives its name to the series, coincides with one of the equiuoxes. Without this junction no Nakṣatra can lead, so to say, the other Nakṣatras, or be seen there at the year-beginning.

1 *The Story of the Heavens* (revised ed., 1913), pp. 493, 494 by Sir Robert S. Ball, F.R.S., Lowndean Professor of Astronomy and Geometry in the University of Cambridge and Director of the Cambridge Observatory

The argument of Pole Star therefore as an evidence of the antiquity of the Vedic literature must be considered valid and J. given the credit of pointing out the same. The custom referred to in the *Gṛhya-Sūtras* is a reminiscence of an earlier tradition prevalent before the Vedic times, and 3000 B. C. is a lower limit of those times.

CHAPTER 3

A. Manu's Accession

195. In considering the chronology of the ancient Aryan kings of India, it has been stated[1] that the accession of Manu, the progenitor of a race that ruled in India, was at about 4000 B. C. It was worked cut in the following manner.

Accession of Manu about 4000 B. C.

The accession to the throne by Candra Gupta Maurya is an historical event, and a landmark for determining the reigns of kings that preceded him. His date is 322 B. C. The dynasties that ruled before him and the durations of their reigns are given below:

1. 9 Nandas	100 years
2. 6 Śiśunāgas (from Bimbisāra to Mahānandin)	169[2] ,,
3. 4 Śiśunāgas (Śiśunāga to Kṣatraujas)	
4. 5 Pradyotas	
5. 22 Bṛhadrathas after Bhārata war	
6. 93 Kings before Bhārata War	
7. 1 Manu	
125 (adding 3 to 7) kings @ an average of 27 years[3] per king	3375 years
Total	3644 years
Add	322 years
Total	3966 years

So Manu's accession is held to have taken place in 3966 B. C. or say 4000 B. C.

1 See my Presidential Address at the 19th Session of the Indian History Congress, held at Agra, 1956, p. 18.

2 Based on historical as distinguished from traditional information.

3 The average of 27 years per king was arrived at by the analogy of the kings of First Dynasty of Babylon. Eduard Meyer, Sidersky, Goetze, Sidney SmithAlbright, Poebel and seven other prominent scholars agree that (eleven) kings of the dynasty reigned for 300 years. It turns out to be 27·27 years per king. I adopt this figure. ·27 is given up as a matter of caution to cover the probable omissions of names. See A. Toynbee, *A Study of History*, vol. X (1954), pp. 171, 172.

B. Sacrifice as an old Institution

Sacrifices of Manu are mentioned in the *Ṛgveda*.

196. Sacrifices performed by Manu are referred to in the following verses of the *Ṛgveda*.[1]

In Maṇḍala 1.

(१) आ नो बर्हीं रिशादसो वरुणो मित्रो अर्यमा ।
सीदन्तु मनुषो यथा ॥

I, 26. 4

[Let Veruṇa, Mitra, and Aryaman sit down upon our sacred grass, as they did at the sacrifice of Manus.—vol. I, p. 68].

(२) मनुष्वदग्ने अङ्गिरस्वदङ्गिरो ययातिवत् सदने पूर्ववच्छुचे ।
अच्छ याह्या वहा दैव्यं जनमा सादय बर्हिषि यक्षि च प्रियम् ॥

I. 31. 17

[Pure Agni, who goes about (to receive oblations), go, in thy presence, to the hall of sacrifice, as did Manus, and Aṅgiras, and Yayāti, and others of old. Bring hither the divine personages; seat them on the sacred grass; and offer them grateful (sacrifice).—vol. I, p. 84].

(3) यं त्वा देवासो मनवे दधुरिह यजिष्ठं हव्यवाहन ।
यं कण्वो मेध्यातिथिर्धनस्पृतं यं वृषा यमुपस्तुतः ॥

I. 36. 10

[Bearer of oblations, (thou art he) whom the gods detained, for the sake of Manu; whom, giver of wealth, Kaṇwa, the host of pious guests, has detained; whom Indra detained; and whom (now), some other worshipper has detained.—vol. I, p. 102).

(4) नि त्वामग्ने मनुर्दधे ज्योतिर्जनाय शश्वते ।
दीदेथ कण्व ऋतजात उक्षितो यं नमस्यन्ति कृष्टयः ॥

I. 36. 19

[Manu detained thee, Agni, (to give) light to the various races of mankind. Born for the sake of sacrifice, and satiated with oblations, thou, whom men reverence, hast blazed for Kanwa.—vol. I, p. 104].

1 The texts are all from Max Müller's edition of the *Rigveda Saṁhitā*. The translations consulted are Wilson's—vol. I (2nd ed. 1866), vol. 2 (1854), vol. 3 (1857), vol. 4 (1866), vol. 5 (1888) and vol. 6 (1888). Max Müller's ramarks regarding sacrifice are worth quoting. It runs thus: "I do not mean to say that the sacrifice as such, was not as old and primitive an institution as sacred poetry itself".—Max Müler, *History*, p. 250

(5) नि त्वा यज्ञस्य साधनमग्ने होतारमृत्विजम् ।
मनुष्वद्देव धीमहि प्रचेतसं जीरं दूतममर्त्यम् ॥
I. 44. 11

[We place thee, Agni, as Manus placed thee, who art the implement of sacrifice, the invoker, the ministering priest, very wise, the destroyer (of foes), immortal, the messenger (of the gods). —vol. I, p. 120]

(6) यथा विप्रस्य मनुषो हविर्भिर्देवाँ अयजः कविभिः कविः सन् ।
एवा होतः सत्यतर त्वमद्याग्ने मन्द्रया जुह्वा यजस्व ॥
I. 76. 5

[As, at the sacrifice of holy Manus, thou, a sage amongst sages, didst worship the gods with oblations, so, also, Agni, veracious invoker of the gods, do thou to-day (present the oblations) with an exhilarating ladle.—vol. I, p. 199].

(7) अग्ने तव त्यदुक्थ्यं देवेष्वस्त्याप्यम् ।
स नः सत्तो मनुष्वदा देवान्यक्षि विदुष्टरो वित्तं मे अस्य रोदसी ॥
I. 105. 13

[Worthy of praise, Agni, is that thy relationship (with the gods). Do thou, who art most wise, seated at our (solemnity), worship (the gods), as (at the sacrifice of) Manus.—vol. I, p. 273].

(8) सत्तो होता मनुष्वदा देवाँ अच्छा विदुष्टरः ।
अग्निर्हव्या सुषूदति देवो देवेषु मेधिरो वित्तं मे अस्य रोदसी ॥
I. 105. 14

[May that wise and liberal Agni, a sage amongst the gods, seated at our rite, as at the sacrifice of Manus, be the invoker of the deities, and offer them oblations. Heaven and earth be conscious of this (my affliction).—vol. I, p. 274].

In Maṇḍala 2.

(9) ज्ञेया भागं सहसानो वरेण त्वादूतासो मनुवद्वदेम ।
अनूनमग्निं जुह्वा वचस्या मधुपृचं धनसा जोहवीमि ॥
II. 10. 6

[Overpowering (thy foes) with lustre, mayest thou recognize thy portion: may we, having thee for our messenger, recite (praise) like Manu: desiring wealth, I offer oblation with the sacrificial ladle and with praises, to that entire Agni, who rewards (the worshipper) with the sweet (fruit) of the sacrifice.—vol. 2, p. 229].

In Maṇḍala 3. (10) यथायजो होत्रमग्ने पृथिव्या यथा दिवो जातवेदश्चिकित्वान् ।
एवानेन हविषा यक्षि देवान् मनुष्वद्यज्ञं प्र तिरेममद्य ॥
III. 17. 2

[As thou didst offer the burnt-offering, Agni, (on behalf of) earth, as thou, Jātavedas, who art cognizant (of sacred rites, didst offer sacrifice on behalf) of heaven; so with this oblation worship the gods, and perfect this rite today (as thou didst) that of Manu.—vol. 3, p. 18].

In Maṇḍala 4. (11) ऋयुदायं देवहितं यथा वः स्तोमो वाजा ऋभुक्षणो ददे वः ।
जुह्वे मनुष्वदुपरासु विक्षु युष्मे सचा बृहद्दिवेषु सोमम् ॥
IV. 37. 3

[As the offering suited to the gods at the third (daily) sacrifice supports you, Vājas, Ṛibhukshans; as the praise (then recited supports you); therefore, like Manu, I offer you the *Soma* juice, along with the very radiant (deities) among the people assembled at the solemnity.—vol. 3. pp. 193, 194].

In Maṇḍala 5. (12) मनुष्वत्त्वा नि धीमहि मनुष्वत् समिधीमहि ।
अग्ने मनुष्वदङ्गिरो देवान् देवयते यज ॥
V. 21. 1

[Like Manu, we meditate, Agni, upon thee; like Manu, we kindle thee: worship the gods on behalf of the (worshipper), devout as Manu.—vol. 3, p. 266]

In Maṇḍala 6. (13) द्युतानं वो अतिथिं स्वर्णरमग्निं होतारं मनुषः स्वध्वरम् ।
विप्रं न द्युक्षवचसं सुवृक्तिभिर्हव्यवाहमरतिं देवमृञ्जसे ॥
VI. 15. 4

[Propitiate with pious praises the radiant Agni, your guest, the guide to heaven, the invoker of the gods (at the sacrifice) of Manu, the celebrator of holy rites, the speaker of brilliant words like a learned sage, thc bearer of oblations (to the gods), the lord, the divine.—vol. 3, p. 404].

(14) त्वं होता मनुर्हितो वह्निरासा विदुष्टरः ।
अग्ने यक्षि दिवो विशः ॥
VI. 16. 9

[Thou hast been appointed by Manu, the invoker of the gods, the most wise bearer of oblations (to them) by thy mouth: worship, Agni, the people of heaven.—vol. 4, pp. 408, 409].

(15) श्रुष्टी वां यज्ञ उद्यतः सजोषा मनुष्वद्वृक्तबर्हिषो यजध्यै ।
आ य इन्द्रावरुणाविषे अद्य महे सुम्नाय मह आववर्तत् ॥
VI. 68 1

[Mighty Indra and Varuṇa, promptly has the *Soma* returned, engaged conscientiously (with the priests) to offer sacrifice to you to obtain food for him by whom, like Manu, the sacred grass has been clipped: he who (invited you hither) today for exceeding happiness.—vol. 4, p. 14].

In Maṇḍala 7.

(16) इळेन्यं वो असुरं सुदक्षमन्तर्दूतं रोदसी सत्यवाचं ।
मनुष्वदग्निं मनुना समिद्धम् समध्वराय सदमिन्महेम ॥
VII. 2. 3

[Let us ever worship the Agni, who is to be adored by us, the mighty, the dextrous, the messenger passing between heaven and earth, the speaker of truth, kindled (of old) by Manu, as now by men, that (he may come) to the solemnity.—vol. 4, p. 33].

(17) त्रिश्चिदक्तोः प्र चिकितुर्वसूनि त्वे अन्तर्दाशुषे मर्त्याय ।
मनुष्वदग्न इह यक्षि देवान् भवा नो दूतो अभिशस्तिपावा ॥
VII. 11. 3

[In thee, Agni, thrice in the day, (the priests) make manifest the treasures (of the oblation) for the (benefit of the) mortal donor: worship the gods on this occasion, Agni, as (thou didst) for Manu: be our messenger, our protector against malignity.—vol. 4, p. 48].

In Maṇḍala 8.

(18) यद्वा यज्ञं मनवे संमिमिक्षथुरेवेत् काण्वस्य बोधतम् ।
बृहस्पतिं विश्वान् देवाँ अहं हुव इन्द्राविष्णू अश्विनावाशुहेषसा ॥
VIII. 10. 2

[In like manner, as you have prepared, Aświns, the sacrifice for Manu, consent (to prepare it) for the son of Kanwa); for I invoke Bṛhaspati, the universal gods, Indra and Vishṇu, and the Aświns with rapid steeds.—vol. 4, p. 261].

(19) यो हव्यान्यैरयता मनुर्हितो देव आसा सुगन्धिना ।
विवासते वार्याणि स्वध्वरो होता देवो अमर्त्यः ॥
VIII. 19. 24

[The divine (Agni), established by Manu, the offerer of the sacrifice, the invoker (of the gods), the divine, the immortal, who conveys the oblations in his fragrant mouth, bestows (upon the adorers) desirable (riches).—vol. 4, p. 294].

20

(20) उशना काव्यस्त्वा नि होतारमसादयत् ।
आयजि त्वा मनवे जातवेदसम् ॥

VIII. 23. 17

[Uśanas, the son of Kavi, has established thee, Jātavedas, as the ministrant priest, thee, as the offerer of sacrifice, for Manu — vol. 5, p. 11].

(21) वयं वो वृक्तबर्हिषो हितप्रयस आनुषक् ।
सुतसोमासो वरुण हवामहे मनुष्वदिद्धाग्नयः ॥

VIII. 27. 7

[Bearing the clipt sacred grass, offering in due order the (sacrificial) food, presenting the effused *Soma* and having the fires kindled, we invoke you, Varuṇa, (and the rest) as did Manus.— vol. 5, p. 29].

(22) यदद्य सूर उदिते यन्मध्यन्दिन आतुचि ।
वामं धत्थ मनवे विश्ववेदसो जुह्वानाय प्रचेतसे ॥

VIII. 27. 21

[Gods), who are possessed of all wealth, bestow the desired (opulence) upon the intelligent Manu, offering oblations to you at sunrise, mid-day and sunset.—vol. 6, p. 31].

In Maṇḍala 9.

(23) यथापवथा मनवे वयोधा अमित्रहा वरिवोविद्धविष्मान् ।
एवा पवस्व द्रविणं दधान इन्द्रे सं तिष्ठ जनयायुधानि ॥

IX 96. 12

[As thou didst flow to Manu possessing food, slaying enemies, acquiring wealth, having oblations, so now flow bringing us riches; abide thou in Indra; make manifest (thy) weapons.—vol, 6, pp. 367, 368].

In Maṇḍala 10.

(24) एहि मनुर्देवयुर्यज्ञकामोऽरंकृत्या तमसि क्षेष्यग्ने ।
सुगान् पथः कृणुहि देवयानान् वह हव्यानि सुमनस्यमानः ॥

X. 51. 5

[(The gods): Come Agni, the devout Manu (is) desirous of offering sacrifice; adorning thyself, thou abidest in darkness; make straight the paths traversed by the gods; and with a benevolent mind convey our oblations.[1]—vol. 6, p. 137].

1 In this hymn, Agni and Viśvadevas, alternately in the even and odd verses, are speaking. Agni seems to be fleeing in fear of hotṛ, and gods make him fearless and grant him his desire so that he may come to the sacrifice of Manu.

(25) उत त्या मे रौद्रावर्चिमन्ता नासत्याविन्द्र गूर्तये यजध्यै ।
मनुष्वद्वृक्तबर्हिषे रराणा मन्दू हितप्रयसा विक्षु यज्यू ॥
X 61. 15

[And, Indra, let those two brilliant sons of Rudra, the Nāsatyas, (be present) at my praise and sacrifice; being propitious to (me seated) on the strewn grass, as (at the sacrfice of) Manu, cheerful, liberal of wealth to the people, deserving of adoration.—vol. 6, p. 161].

(26) येभ्यो होत्रां प्रथमामायेजे मनुः समिद्धाग्निर्मनसा सप्त होतृभिः ।
त आदित्या अभयं शर्म यच्छत सुगा नः कर्त सुपथा स्वस्तये ॥
X. 63. 7

[Ādityas, to whom Manu, having kindled the fire, offered the first sacrifice with (reverent) mind (aided) by the seven ministrant priests, do you bestow upon us prosperity, free from peril; provide for us pleasant paths easy to travel for our well-being.—vol. 6, p. 169].

(27) तिस्रो देवीर्बर्हिरिदं वरीय आ सीदत चकृमा वः स्योनम् ।
मनुष्वद्यज्ञं सुधिता हवींषीळा देवी घृतपदी जुषन्त ॥
X. 70. 8

[Sit down, you three goddesses, upon this broad *Barhis*, we have spread it out for you; Ilā, radiant (Saraswati) and bright-footed (Bhāratī), accept our sacrifice and well-presented oblations as if they were Manu's.—vol. 6, p. 193],

(28) तदिद्ध्यस्य सवनं विवेरपो यथा पुरा मनवे गातुमश्रेत् ।
गोअर्णसि त्वाष्ट्रे अश्वनिर्णिजि प्रेमध्वरेष्वध्वराँ अशिश्रयुः ॥
X. 76. 3

[May this (sacrificial) work of this grinding-stone, the effusion of the *Soma*, spread as it went formerly along the path to Manu; when the son of Twashtṛi, hidden by the (stolen) cows, and assuming the form of a horse, (was to be slain), the worshippers had recourse at the sacrifices to the inviolable (upper grinding-stones).—vol. 6, pp. 206, 207].[1]

1 Cf. the following

मनुर्ह वा अग्रे यज्ञेनेजे तदनुकृत्येमाः प्रजा यजन्ते तस्मादाह मनुष्वदिति मनोर्यज्ञ इत्यु वा आहुः ॥

Śatapatha, Br., I. 5. 1. 7

'Like as Manu (did), like as Bharata';—Manu, indeed, worshipped with sacrifice in olden times, and doing as he did these descendants of his now sacrifice; therefore he says 'like as Manu'. Or, say they, (it means) 'at the sacrifice of Manu', and therefore he says 'as (he did) with Manu'.

J. Eggeling, The Śatapatha-Brāhmaṇa (S.B.E., vol. xii)(Transl.), pt. I. p. 133

Two broad groups of verses mentioning Manu's sacrifices.

197. The above verses may be arranged in two broad groups, viz. (1) those that indicate that Manu's sacrifice took place at the time of or a little earlier than the composition of the verses, and (2) those that indicate that they were composed many generations after Manu's sacrifice. This points to the chronological sequence of the sacrifices by Manu or other kings after him from about 4000 B. C. downwards.

Sacrifices thus existed before the time of Manu as evidenced by the developed stage at which we find them during the period. The use of the term Darśa-pūrṇamāsaḥ[1] and Atirātra (a ritual connected with Sattra) indicates that at the time of the *Ṛgveda*, sacrifices reached a developed stage. Moreover, the whole of the 9th Maṇḍala of the *Ṛgveda* is devoted to the delineation of the Soma sacrifice. The verse no. 23 (*Rv.*, IX. 96) mentioned above contains a prayer to the Soma for flowing towards the performer of the sacrifice as it had done in the past towards Manu. All this can only mean that sacrifice was an institution older than the *Ṛgveda* itself.

Gradually, sacrifices occupied a very important place in the religious practices of ancient Indo-Aryans. A close connection was early established between the sacrifices and heavenly bodies,—the sun, the moon and the Nakṣatras. In paras 148-150, the nature of the important role played by the 27 asterics in connection with the religious life of the people has been described in detail.

B. The Indian Origin of Nakṣatras

Discussion which continued for a long period centred round the question as to whether the Indo-Aryans had borrowed the conception of 27 Nakṣatras from any other country.

198. The question naturally arises as to whether the Nakṣatras of the Vedas were indigeneous or borrowed. M. has examined the problem elaborately and come to the definite conclusion that the Nakṣatras were absolutely of Indian origin.[2] Had this conclusion been otherwise, in other words had the Nakṣatras been proved to be of foreign origin, then possibly the different kinds of sacrifices, the gods worshipped at these sacrifices and the hymns repeated at

1 "There are several hymns which contain allusions to the Darśapūrṇamāsa, the famous New and Full Moon sacrifices. These sacrifices in themselves may have been of the greatest antiquity, as old as any attempt at a regulated worship of the gods".—Max Müller, *History*, p. 253

2 *Preface* to the *Ṛgveda Text.*, ed. by Max Müller, vol. IV (1862), pp. xxviii-lxxi

annual festivals would have all become borrowed. And if the source be Chinese from which the ancient Indian astronomy was borrowed, as suggested by Biot, W. and some others, all our received ideas on the earliest history of mankind would be upset.[1]

Biot, the French Astronomer, is in favour of Chinese origin. Lassen supports him.

Biot (1774-1862), an eminent French astronomer, was a great advocate of Chinese origin of Indian Nakṣatras. According to him, the original number of the Nakṣatras was 28. Reduced afterwards to 27, they did not represent the 27 divisions of the ecliptic at first and had no connection with the course of the moon. Lassen[2] supports Biot's views that Chinese Nakṣatras were introduced to India in the 14th century B. C. As the Chinese stars were however only 24 in number, he overcomes this difficulty by stating that the Chinese principle was adopted in the 14th century and the number was not raised to 27 till 1100 B. C.

Hardwick agrees with Biot.

Hardwick[3] also was of the same opinion. In a review[4] of Hardwick's book shortly afterwards, M. protested against the theory of foreign origin of Indian Nakṣatras. He pointed out that astronomy, particularly the subject of Nakṣatras, is most intimately connected with the religious writings of the Veda, that Hindu sacrifice could not have been properly performed without a knowledge of the lunar mansions, and that no month could have received its present appellation without names being first given to those constellations from which the months derived their titles.

Max Müller answers, and disproves the Chinese origin of the Indian list of Nakṣatras.

"The Nakshatras are mentioned in the ancient songs of the Veda. Thus *RV.* (I. 50. 2) has 'like thieves the Nakshatras (the stars) depart every night, before the sun who illuminates everything.' Here it might be said that Nakshatra signified stars in general, and not the twenty-seven constellations rendered important by the passage of the moon. But it is in connexion with the moon, and therefore with an allusion to an equally divided lunar zodiac, that the Nakshatras are mentioned in the Veda. 'Soma, or the moon,' it is said, in a hymn of the tenth Maṇḍala (X, 85, 2) 'is placed in the lap of the Nakshatras'.

1 *Ibid.*, p. xxxviii 2 Lassen, *Indian Antiquities*, p. 747

3 Hardwick, *An Historical Inquiry into some of the chief Parallelisms and Contrasts between Christianity and the Religious Systems of the Ancient World*, 1855-1858, pp. 7, 8

4 Max Müller, *Preface* to the Rigveda Text, vol. IV, p. xl

The moon is called the month-maker, māsakrid, in the first book of the Rig-veda, at least according to one of the commentators; and one of the principal sacrifices, mentioned in the ceremonial portion of the Veda, is that of the Full and New moon. The exact time of these lunar festivals is fixed with such minute accuracy, that the Hindus, at the time when these public sacrifices were established, or at least when they were regulated by the sacred institutions of the Brāhamaṇas, must have been considerably advanced in astronomy; and the base of their ancient astronomy was the zodiac of the lunar Nakshatras."[1]

The fact that the moon and the month are synonymous terms in the dialects of ancient Aryan family leads M. to suggest that the division of the year into lunar months must have been made when the Aryan family had not separated. M. points out at the same time, however, that the name of each month is particularly Indian and found in Sanskrit only, and that as Indian months are all derived from Nakṣatras which again had been derived from ancient Vedic deities, so the conclusion becomes irresistible that the Nakṣatras were Indian in origin.

If there had been any borrowing, it was the Chinese who borrowed from the Indians, according to M., for no Chinese dictionary is able to explain how the following names of Indian Nakṣatras got into the list of Chinese Sieu: Pehoua-Pauṣa, Makue-Māgha, Pholkuna-Phālguna. M. therefore thinks that the natural conclusion should be that they were borrowed by the Chinese[2]. A reference to Chinese history corroborates, according to M., this conclusion. For, the emperor Tsin-Chu-houng who reigned in China after Hans dynasty in 206 B. C. destroyed Chinese literature, including astronomy[3]. It is therefore not possible to indicate the state of astronomical knowledge before that date, not to speak of its being borrowed by India.

M. also dismisses the idea that Greeks had any influence on the ancient Hindu astronomy. Words decidedly of Greek character found in Sanskrit must be of very late date, say after intercourse was established between India and Greece after Alexander's invasion, states M.[4]

1 *Ibid.*, xl
2 *Ibid.*, p. xli,
3 *Ibid.*, p. xliii
4 *Ibid.*, pp. xliii, xliv

Biot persists in holding his theory and is supported by Whitney.

199. In spite of the above review by M., Biot persisted in his theory, and soon won the approval of W. who changed it a little. According to W. the 24 Chinese stars were not directly imported from China, but the whole system with 28 Nakṣatras came to India not much later than 1100 B. C. (Sūrya-Siddhānta, pp. 201-203)[1].

Max Müller shows why Biot and Whitney cannot be accepted.

200. M. rejects W.'s theory of indirect import of the stars of China, as well as Weber's theory of Babylon being the common source from which both China and India borrowed.[2]

In order to understand the Hindu astronomy properly, it is necessary, according to M., to bear in mind the three following fundamental facts:

(I) The moon's passage, i.e., its sidereal motion suggested to Hindus the number of Nakṣatras to be 27.[3] M. offers the following explanation as to why the moon's position was given so much importance in those early days.

"Nothing was more natural for the sake of counting days, months and seasons, than to observe the twenty-seven places which the moon occupied in her passage from any point of the sky back to the same point. It was far easier than to determine the sun's position from day to day, or from month to month, for the stars being hardly visible at the rising and setting of the sun, the idea of the sun's conjunction with certain stars could not suggest itself to a listless observer. The moon, progressing from night to night, and coming successively in contact with certain stars, was like the finger of a clock, moving round a circle, and coming in contact with one figure after another."[4]

2) The Nakṣatras were intended to mark certain equal divisions of the heavens. Their number being 27, each covered 13° 20° (360° ÷ 27).

3) The number of Nakṣatras was originally, and in one sense always, 27 and not 28.[5]

1 *Ibid.*, xliv
2 *Ibid.*, p. xlv-xlvi
3 *Ibid.*, p. xliv
4 *Ibid.*, pp. li, lii
5 *Ibid.*, p. xlvii

201. Weber (*Nakṣatras,* p. 320) discovered a thorough analogy or even identity of both the Chinese and the Indian systems which are unacceptable to M. for the following reasons:

Max Müller quotes authorities. Weber.

1) The Chinese Sieus were originally 24 in number, raised afterwards to 28, whereas the number of Indian Nakṣatras was 27. No trace can be found anywhere in the Indian literature of a change similar to what took place in China.

2) The Sieus are all single stars, whereas the Indian Nakṣatras are mostly groups or clusters of stars.

3) If the Hindus were really the pupils of the Chinese, the whole of 28 sieus would have been borrowed by India, and not a portion only as is suggested by Biot.[1]

202. A passage from Colebrooke's *Miscellaneous Essays,* II, 447 is quoted by M. in support of his own theory.[2] Bentley also thinks that an attempt to identify Chinese sieus with Indian Nakṣatras is futile, specially because the lunar mansions of the Hindus invariably contain 13° 20' each, whereas those of the Chinese are of various extent from a few minutes to 30° and upwards.[3]

Colebrooke. Bentley.

203. M. admits that the exact number of Nakṣatras, though frequently mentioned in the *Brāhmaṇas,* is not definitely stated in the Chandas or Mantra period. In the list of names of the Nakṣatras and their deities in the *Taittirīya-Saṃhitā,* (VI. 4. 10) or in the *Taittirīya-Brāhmaṇa,* (I. 5. 1. 27) Nakṣatras are found, but no mention is made of the Nakṣatra Abhijit. The *Taittirīya-Brāhmaṇa* (IV. 2. 1. 6) gives the name of the Nakṣatra for the first time.[4] All this leads M. to deny foreign influence on the nomen-

Max Müller denies foreign influence on the nomenclature of Nakṣatras.

1 *Ibid.,* pp. xlviii, xlix

2 The passage runs thus:

"The Hindus had undoubtedly made some progress at an early period in the astronomy cultivated by them for the regulation of time. Their calendar, both civil and religious, was generated chiefly, not exclusively, by the moon and the sun; and the motions of these luminaries were carefully observed by them and with such success, that their determination of the moon's synodical revolution, which was what they were principally concerned with, is a much more correct one than the Greeks ever achieved. They had a division of the ecliptic into twenty-seven and twenty-eight (?) parts, suggested evidently by the moon's period in days, and seemingly their own; it was certainly borrowed by the Arabians." *Ibid.,* p. xlix

3 *Ibid.,* p. li.

4 *Ibid.,* pp. lvi-lxvii

clature of Indo-Aryan Nakṣatras. He goes further and declares that the "spring-heads of the thought, of the language, and of the poetry of India, rise from the depths inaccessible to foreign tributaries, and the earliest course may be followed step by step with greater accuracy than in the case of the early history of any other nation."[1]

It is to be added that the view expressed by M. is correct inasmuch as the existence of sacrifice as an established institution at the time of Manu at about 4000 B. C. corroborates the antiquity of the Indian Nakṣatras, for the timing of the sacrifices was connected with the moon and the stars.

C. The Art of Writing in Ancient India

1. *Max Müller*

Writing was unknown before the time of Pāṇini (Max Müller).

204. M. poses the question, "Was the collection of the ten books of Vedic hymns the work of persons cognisant of the art of writing or not? Were 1017 hymns of the *Ṛgveda*, after they had been gathered into one body, preserved by memory, or on paper?"[2]

Both in his *History*[3] and *Preface* to his edition of Vedic texts,[4] M. expresses the opinion that before the time of Pāṇini, and before the spread of Buddhism in India, "Writing for literary purposes was absolutely unknown." M. advances the following reasons for his theory:

1) Historically, it has been found that the preservation of truly national poetry of principal nations of antiquity was everywhere due to the unaided efforts of memory.[5]

2) "Where writing is known, it is almost impossible to compose a thousand hymns without bringing in some such words as, writing, reading, paper or pen. Yet there is not one single allusion in these hymns to anything connected with writing."[6] As evidence, M. quotes from *The Old Testament*, and the *Psalms* which indicate knowledge of writing on the part of the Jews. A comparison is made with the Homeric poems which do not contain a single mention of writing, though after Homer, "writing was a common acquirement of the educated classes of Greece,"[6] and

1 *Ibid.*, pp. lxx, lxxi
2 Max Müller, *History*, p. 257
3 *Ibid.*, p, 262
4 Max Müller, *Preface to the Ṛgveda Saṃhitā* (Text), vol. IV, p. lxxxi
5 Max Müller, *History*, p. 257
6 *Ibid.*, p. 258

Greece used to import paper from Egypt. According to M., "the total absence of any allusion to writing may safely be supposed to prove the absence of the art at the time when that literature arose." Nor does he find any allusion to writing during the whole of the Brāhmaṇa period.[1] In his opinion, even during the Sūtra period, "The whole literature of India was preserved by oral tradition only."[2]

3) M. finds further corroboration of his theory in the fact that in ancient India the only occupation of people of the three high castes was the study of the Vedas for 12 years by those who wanted to marry and 48 years by those who remained celebates.[3] M. describes the way the Veda was learnt. According to him long years were necessary in order that the sacred songs might be preserved and guarded against loss and corruption.[4] Every event of the life of a Brāhmin, he states, is depicted in the *Gṛhya-sūtrās* but not a word is found in them about his learning to write.

M. therefore concludes that the hymns of the *Ṛgveda* and other Vedic literature were carried from generation to generation by oral tradition.

2. *Wilson*

Wilson gives reasons for holding the same view.

205. Wilson is also almost of the same view. "This is the more remarkable, as there can be little doubt that the hymns were taught, originally, orally, and that the knowledge of them was perpetuated by the same mode of tuition."[5] He mentions several characteristics of these hymns, such as their very construction; abundance of elliptical phrases; use of general epithets whose application, unless explained, is far from obvious; brief comparisons that cannot be appreciated until supplied by a competent leader; the innumerable blanks and deficiencies that make the text of the Vedas unintelligible in many places which the Scholiast alone can fill up with greater or less fidelity according to what he has received as tradition. The consideration of the above facts

1 Max Müller mentions Wolf (Prolegomena, lxx-lxxiii) as declaring that prose composition is a safe sign of a written literature, but M. holds that it is not so in the case of India.

2 Max Müller, *History*, p. 259

3 *Ibid.*, pp. 259, 260

4 *Ibid.*, p. 261

5 *Ṛgveda Saṃhita, a collection of ancient Hindu Hymns.* The first Ashṭaka or Book of Rigveda (Tr.), *Preface*, pp. xviii, xix

leads Wilson to believe that a living teacher or commentator was indispensable to right understanding of the meaning of the Sūktas from the moment of their first communication, and that the probability is in favour of an oral instructor.[1]

3. Bühler

Bühler is prepared to push back the date of the writing to 1000 B. C. which might be modified on further explorations.

206. B. has considered the whole question from Paleograhical point of view. At the outset, he admits that in this respect the orthodox as well as heterodox sects of India are of one opinion, viz. that writing or at least the chief script is very old in India. Al Beruni is referred to as stating that Hindus once knew the art of writing, but forgot it somehow, till through divine inspiration Vyāsa, the son of Parāśara, rediscovered the same, If this view were correct, then B. has to push back the Indian alphabets to the beginning of Kaliyuga in 3101 B. C. in deference to Al Beruni.[2]

B. does not attach any importance to this tradition. He finds that the Brāhmī script, which is adopted by the alphabets of the most of the dialects of India, has its origin in North Semitic signs, which again appear in the archaic Phoenician inscriptions[3]. As to the time when India borrowed this script, B. is of the view that elaboration of the alphabets was completed in 500 B. C. or earlier still, and the *terminum a quo* is about 800 B. C. B. is careful enough to state that the above estimate was a provisional one, which may be modified by discovery of new epigraphic documents in India or the Semitic countries. At the time when B. made the above statement, Marshall's discoveries in Mohenjo Daro had not begun and nobody could think that a script dating between 4000 and 3000 B. C. would be met with. How prophetic therefore B. seems to be when he made the following utterances in connection with the same topic: "If such a modification should become necessary, the results of the recent finds induce one to believe that the date of the introduction will prove to fall earlier, and that it will have to be fixed perhaps in the tenth century B. C. or even before that."[4]

1 *Ibid.*, p. xix
2 G. Bühler, *Indian Paleography from about B.C. 350 to A.D. 1300.*
3 *Ibid.*, p. 15
4 *Ibid.*, p. 17

Our Viewpoint

Re. Writing in Ancient India

Max Müller, Wilson and Bühler on writing in early times.

207. In spite of an emphatic assertion that Vedic Indo-Aryans did not know the art of writing, M. refers to teaching at the time of the *Ṛgveda* in the following manner. M. states that writing or even teaching is not mentioned in the primitive poetry of Chandas period, and that the earliest allusion to oral teaching occurs in a Ṛgvedic hymn that is ascribed by him to the Mantra period,—Hymn VII. 103 (Frog Song). He states that in a satirical verse on the Vasiṣṭhas (VII. 103. 5) the frogs are compared with Brāhmaṇs teaching their pupils: "one frog repeats the words of another, like a pupil who repeats the words of his teacher. No similar allusion to writing is to be found even in the latest hymns, the so-called Khilas."[1] The verse runs as follows:

यदेषामन्यो अन्यस्य वाचं शाजस्येव वदति शिक्षमाणः ।
सर्वं तदेषां समृध्वेव पर्व यतसुवाचो वदथनाव्धप्सु ॥

Rv. VII. 103.5

[When one of you imitates the croaking of another as a learner (imitates) his teacher, when, loud crying, you converse (leaping) upon the waters, then the entire body is as it were developed].[2]

In regard to knowledge of the art of writing on the part of ancient Indo-Aryans, Wilson, as we have seen, speaks of a *probability* in favour of an oral instructor, because that would be most in harmony with the unconnected and unsystematic "currency of the hymns." He further restricts his proposition by adding, "with the restricted use of writing,—even if the art were known in those early times (a subject of considerable doubt)".[3] What Wilson means to state is that even if writing were known in those ancient times, the oral instructor would have been indispensable. He does not completely rule out the idea of writing being known at the time.

Had B. lived to see the discoveries of Mohenjo Daro, it is probable that he would have placed the invention of writing at a much earlier period.

1 Max Müller, *History*, pp. 261, 262
2 Wilson, *Ṛgveda*, Trnsl. vol. 4, p. 203
3 *Ibid. Preface*, p. xix

The vast Vedic literature, specially its prose portion, and familiarity with script by Mohenjo Daro people incline us to push back the date to 4000 B.C.

208. In this connection, the following two points should also be duly considered so as to come to a right conclusion as to whether or not the ancient Indo-Aryans used writing as an art for literary purposes:

I. As far as the hymns of the *Ṛgveda* are concerned, it is possible that they used to be sung and handed down from generation to generation at the beginning. But when the Mantra period arrived the songs must have grown in volume (more than 1000 hymns as we have them now), and it naturally became more and more difficult to preserve this vast lore intact. Further, when the Brāhmaṇa period emerged, and a vast prose literature including one that contained details about sacrifices appeared, it could not be expected to endure without being written down. We shall therefore be not wrong if we suppose that writing was introduced in the times of the Brāhmaṇa period, if not earlier.

II. The discovery of Indus script has further strengthened the hands of those who think that writing was known to Indo-Aryans long before 1000 B.C. Indeed, it is not conceivable that people on one side of the Indus were conversant with this art and those on the other side were not. The inference should rather be the contrary.

209. It is difficult to understand why M. does not accept Wolf's theory,[1] that prose composition of a people is a sure sign of a written literature, specially when the extant vedic prose composition is so vast. No conclusion either way is permissible from a non-mention of writing in the Vedic literature. Its existence must be inferred from other evidences, particularly as the custom with the Ṛgvedic poets is not to mention directly an important event such as year, seasons, intercalation, etc. Of course it is not denied that the form of the script used for writing the *Ṛgveda* and other Vedic literature may be more archaic, but there is no doubt that it was the forerunner of the present script.

Conclusion.

1 See para 204 (fn. at p. 156)

208. In this connection, the following two points should also be duly considered so as to come to a right conclusion, as to whether or not the ancient Indo-Aryans used writing as an art for literary purposes.

The last Vedic literature, especially prose portion, and familiarity with [illegible] by means of a [illegible] period before us to [illegible] the 1000 to 800 B.C.

I. In so far as the hymns of the Rgveda are concerned, it is possible that they had to be sung and handed down from generation to generation in the beginning. But when the Mantra period arrived, the songs which have grown in volume to more than 1000 hymns as we have them now, and it naturally became more and more difficult to preserve this vast lore intact. Further, when the Brahmana period emerged, and a vast prose literature including one that contained details about sacrifices appeared, it could not be expected to survive without being written down. We shall therefore be not wrong if we suppose that writing was introduced in the times of the Brahmanas, if not earlier.

II. The discovery of Indus script has further strengthened the hands of those who think that writing was known to Indo-Aryans long before 1000 B.C. Indeed, it is not conceivable that people on one side of the Indus were conversant with this art and those on the other side were not. The inference should rather be the contrary.

209. It is difficult to understand why M. does not accept Weber's theory[1] that prose composition of a people is a sure sign of written literature, especially when the great Vedic prose composition is so vast. No conclusion, either way, is permissible from the non-appearance of writing in the Vedic literature. Its existence must be inferred from other evidences, particularly as the custom with the Rgvedic poets is not to mention directly an important event such as years, seasons, intercalation, etc. Of course it is not claimed that the form of the script used for writing the Rgveda and other Vedic literature may be more ancient; but there is no doubt that it was the precursor of the present script.

Conclusion.

[1] [illegible]

INDEX

The Blurb that appeared in the first reprint of Dr. N. N. Law's "*Aspects of Ancient Indian Polity*" in 1960 published by Messrs Orient Longmans, Calcutta, contains *inter alia* critical remarks on several other books of the author. These remarks are reproduced below by courtesy of Messrs Orient Longmans Private Ltd.

"THE AUTHOR"

Dr. N. N. Law, an historical writer of eminence, the editor of the **Indian Historical Quarterly** for the last 35 years (a very high standard journal of international repute), has dealt with almost all the major periods of Indian History. Commencing his researches in 1911, just after leaving college, he has been engaged in them with unabated energy up till now.

On the appearance of the first book from his pen, **Studies in Ancient Hindu Polity**, 1914, **The Pioneer** of Allahabad wrote an elaborate editorial on the volume (July 2, 1914). The impressions made upon the mind of the learned editor are summed up as follows: "It is a healthy sign that Indian writers are beginning to absorb the critical spirit of the West. Still imperfectly developed among ourselves, it has much leeway to make up in the East, but Mr. Law is a century in advance of his countrymen in accuracy and sobriety of statement." This observation is as true today as it was in 1914.

Coupled with the above qualities is his analytical insight, which enables him to discover things unnoticed by others. For instance all the elements of the present-day law of contract were pointed out by him (see Ch. 10 of **Studies**) as existing in the law relating to contract in the Kauṭilīya Arthaśāstra.

He brought it to the notice of scholars that Vārttā (agriculture or some such means of livelihood in ancient India) was elevated to the rank of one of the four branches of learning, most probably in the Epic Period, i.e, several centuries before Aristotle wrote on the "special science or art of wealth" (**Indian Antiquary**, 1918; also Dr. Law's work **Indian History and Culture**, 1925, pp. 67-93).

It was he who first stated in his **Promotion of Learning in India during Muhammadan Rule** (1916, p. 142) that Akbar was literate, though he had been looked upon as Illiterate by many writers. The distinguished Persian scholar H. Beveridge, who contributed a Foreword to Dr. Law's **Promotion of Learning**, remarked with a mixture of humour and surprise that the author did not believe that Akbar was illiterate. On reading the Foreword, the author by delaying the publication for some time, wrote an Addendum, with further evidence in support of his contention. After this, no reply came from Beveridge. In 1936, came a corroboration of Akbar's literacy in an illustration contained in Ibn Hassan's **Central Structure of the Mughal Empire**, p. 94. This illustration is a copy of the front page of the **Zafar Nama** of Timur. On it there appears Akbar's own handwriting.

The valuable brochure **Inter-State Relations in Ancient India**, 1920, embodies the results of intensive study of a very difficult portion of the Kauṭilīya. The author has removed the obscurity of a number of terms and passages, and thrown much new light on the subject.

K. P. Jayaswal in chapters 37 and 38 of his **Hindu Polity**, 1924 attributes the divison of kingdoms into Paura (Capital) and Janapada (the Country), to the tendency of Indian States to develop "non-national territorial Monarchies." The nature and political powers and functions of the Janapada (Assembly of the Realm not including capital), and Paura (Assembly of the Capital) are treated by him in detail. Dr. Law does away with the bases of these two chapters after an exhaustive examination of each of the direct and indirect evidences adduced by Jayaswal, showing that not a single piece of evidence can stand scrutiny.

In his Address as the President of the 19th Session of the Indian History Congress at Agra, Dec. 1956, the author has thrown new light on the ancient Hindu Royal Genealogies (based on Indian historical tradition), giving strong and cogent reasons for placing the first king Manu at about 4000 B.C.

He has removed long-standing anomalies and misconceptions regarding the genealogies of the Pradyota and the Śiśunāga Dynasties of Magadha. The mistaken conception regarding the Pradyota Dynasty that it belonged to Avanti, prevalent for a number of years among scholars, and found in text-books of Indian educational institutions, was for the first time removed, and the position clarified, by the author. It is time that this as well as the corrections made by him in the genealogy of the Śiśunāga Dynasty of Magadha received a wide recognition.

WORKS

BY

DR. NARENDRA NATH LAW

1. Studies in Ancient Indian Polity, (Longmans, Green & Co., Ltd., London), 1914.
2. Promotion of Learning in India by Early European Settlers (up to 1800 A.D.), (Do), 1915.
3. Promotion of Learning In India (during Muhammadan Rule) by Muhammadans, (Do), 1916.
4. (a) Aspects of Ancient Indian Polity (Oxford at the Clarendon Press), 1921.
4 (b) Aspects of Ancient Indian Polity (first Reprint by Orient Longmans Private Ltd., 1960, Calcutta).
5. Inter-State Relations in Ancient India, 1920.
6. Studies in Indian History and Culture, (Luzac & Co.), 1925.
7. Life of MM. Haraprosad Sastri, 1932.
8. Sri Kṛṣṇa and Sri Caitanya, 1949.
9. প্রাচীন হিন্দু দণ্ডনীতি, ১৯২৩
10. ভারতে শিক্ষাবিস্তার ১৯২৩, (প্রথম ইউরোপীয় অধিবাসীগণের দ্বারা ১৮০০ খৃঃ পর্যন্ত)
11. দেশ বিদেশের ব্যাঙ্ক, ১৯৬০
12. প্রাচীন ভারতীয় রাষ্ট্রসমূহের পরস্পর সম্বন্ধ. ১৯৬১
13. দেশবিদেশের রাষ্ট্রীয় কাঠামো ১ম খণ্ড ১৯৬৬, (আমেরিকা, ফ্রান্স এবং সুইজারল্যাণ্ড)
14. দেশবিদেশের রাষ্ট্রীয় কাঠামো, ২য় খণ্ড, ১৯৬৮ (লণ্ডনে গণতন্ত্রের ক্রম-বিকাশের ইতিহাস)
15. স্বর্ণবণিক কথা ও কীর্তি, ১ম, ২য় ও ৩য় খণ্ড ১৯৪০, ১৯৪১, ১৯৪২ (প্রতি খণ্ড ৫০০ পৃষ্ঠার উপর)
16. শ্রীকৃষ্ণ ও শ্রীচৈতন্য, ১৯৪৭

Journals

17. Indian Historical Quarterly, 38 vols. from 1925
18. স্বর্ণবণিক সমাচার (মাসিক পত্রিকা) ১৯১৬ হইতে ৪৬ বৎসর চলিয়াছে ; (উহার মধ্যে ১৯২৭ সাল হইতে ১৯৫৮ সাল পর্যন্ত অর্থাৎ বত্রিশ খণ্ডের ডঃ লাহা সম্পাদক ছিলেন ।)
19. আর্থিক উন্নতি, ১৯২৬ হইতে ২৩ বৎসর চলিয়াছিল। (এই পত্রিকার আর্থিক দায়িত্ব ন্যস্ত ছিল ডিরেক্টর ডঃ এন. লাহার উপর ।)

In the same Address, he has shown, by giving details and examples, that there is ample scope for writing a history of ancient Indian morals on the lines of Lecky's **History of European Morals.** (See **IHQ**, Dec. 1956).

Besides these many achievements, Dr. Law, a prolific writer, has published several other books and articles.

Aspects of Ancient Indian Polity

"One of the earliest books to be published on the subject, this work is still considered one of the few very authoritative on the subject. Critical and objective, based on original sources, and written from a comparative standpoint, the volume presents a balanced view of the earliest Hindu speculations on the State and the king, the administrative machinery, and other political topics. Nothing that has been written since its first publication in 1921 has outdated this work. The subject is taught at Post-Graduate level in several universities in India, and students and young researchers wil find this book a most useful guide."